Teaching Music History with Cases

Teaching Music History with Cases introduces a pedagogical approach to music history instruction in university coursework.

What constitutes a music-historical "case?" How do we use them in the classroom? In business and the hard sciences, cases are problems that need solutions. In a field like music history, a case is not always a problem, but often an exploration of a context or concept that inspires deep inquiry. Such cases are narratives of rich, complex moments in music history that inspire questions of similar or related moments. This book guides instructors through the process of designing a curriculum based on case studies, finding and writing case studies, and guiding class discussions of cases.

Sara Haefeli is Associate Professor at Ithaca College, New York, and Editor-in-Chief of the *Journal of Music History Pedagogy*. She is the author of *John Cage: A Research and Information Guide*.

Modern Musicology and the College Classroom
Series Editor: James A. Davis, *SUNY Fredonia*

Modern Musicology and the College Classroom is a series of professional titles for current and future college instructors of musicology in its broadest definition—encompassing music history, ethnomusicology, music theory, and music courses for all majors. Volumes feature a basic introduction to a significant field of current scholarship, a discussion of how the topic impacts pedagogical methodology and materials, and pragmatic suggestions for incorporating these ideas directly into the classroom.

Listening Across Borders
Musicology in the Global Classroom
Edited by James A. Davis and Christopher Lynch

Teaching Electronic Music
Cultural, Creative, and Analytical Perspectives
Edited by Blake Stevens

Race and Gender in the Western Music History Survey
A Teacher's Guide
Horace J. Maxile, Jr. and Kristen M. Turner

Music, Gender, and Sexuality Studies
A Teacher's Guide
Jacqueline Warwick

Disability and Accessibility in the Music Classroom
A Teacher's Guide
Alexandria Carrico and Katherine Grennell

Teaching Music History with Cases
A Teacher's Guide
Sara Haefeli

For more information about this series, please visit: www.routledge.com/
Modern-Musicology-and-the-College-Classroom/book-series/MMCC

Teaching Music History with Cases

A Teacher's Guide

Sara Haefeli

Routledge
Taylor & Francis Group

NEW YORK AND LONDON

First published 2023
by Routledge
605 Third Avenue, New York, NY 10158

and by Routledge
4 Park Square, Milton Park, Abingdon, Oxon, OX14 4RN

Routledge is an imprint of the Taylor & Francis Group, an informa business

Library of Congress Cataloging-in-Publication Data
Names: Haefeli, Sara, author. Title: Teaching music history with cases:
a teacher's guide / Sara Haefeli.
Description: [1.] | New York: Routledge, 2023. | Series: Modern musicology
and the college classroom | Includes bibliographical references and index.
Identifiers: LCCN 2022037737 (print) | LCCN 2022037738 (ebook) |
ISBN 9780367672539 (hardback) | ISBN 9780367672546 (paperback) |
ISBN 9781003130482 (ebook)
Subjects: LCSH: Music—History and criticism—Study and teaching (Higher) |
Critical pedagogy.
Classification: LCC MT18 .H234 2023 (print) | LCC MT18 (ebook) |
DDC 780.71—dc23/eng/20220809
LC record available at https://lccn.loc.gov/2022037737
LC ebook record available at https://lccn.loc.gov/2022037738

ISBN: 9780367672539 (hbk)
ISBN: 9780367672546 (pbk)
ISBN: 9781003130482 (ebk)

DOI: 10.4324/9781003130482

Typeset in Times New Roman
by Newgen Publishing UK

To all my students, most especially Keilah, who inspired this journey with one brave conversation.

Contents

Contents

1 Introduction

When I was hired at Ithaca College in 2011, it was primarily on the strength of my teaching, not on my reputation as a scholar. I consider myself among the fortunate to have a true calling as a teacher, and I enjoy being in front of a classroom just as much as I enjoy performing or researching and writing. During the first several years in my current position, I often heard from students who had finished the music history sequence that they really missed my class because "they loved my stories." While they meant it as a compliment, I found these comments troubling. These remarks echoed what I often read on course evaluations: many students loved the class because it was *entertaining*. Students even commented (surprisingly often) on my clothes, as if how I dressed was part of the show! My feeling mirrors that of the English professor Mark Edmundson, who wrote:

> I don't teach to amuse, to divert, or even, for that matter, to be merely interesting. When someone says she "enjoyed" the course—and that word crops up again and again in my evaluations—somewhere at the edge of my immediate complacency I feel encroaching self-dislike. That is not at all what I had in mind.[1]

What Edmundson and I both wish for instead is that students come away from our classes *changed, challenged,* or even *discomforted*.

My discomfort with my music history courses was dialed up during Black Lives Matter protests on my campus in 2015. Conversations with my students revealed, unsurprisingly, that they did not see diversity reflected in the music history curriculum. My students—most of whom were training to be teachers or performers—felt unprepared to work in diverse musical settings. They reported that my assignments and assessment tools often felt inauthentic and that while they found the lectures interesting, they had trouble remembering content or even

DOI: 10.4324/9781003130482-1

discerning from the lecture what was important. Students pointed out that the exclusion of jazz, gospel, and other Black styles as course materials and potential research paper topics was racist. I also knew that students of color failed my classes at far higher rates, even though they were very likely just as capable as their white peers—if perhaps less prepared for college due to widespread educational disparities between white and minoritized communities.[2]

I spent the next year—a sabbatical year—coming to terms with the fact that I wasn't just falling short of my own teaching goals, but that I had actually harmed students who were marginalized by my exclusion of those of their ethnicities from the story of music history I was telling. As I explored options that would diversify my curriculum and engage *all* of my students, I realized that I could not solve this problem by merely adding to the existing curriculum more musical examples from women and people of color. The problem was embedded in my curricular *design*. As I spent the year researching transformative pedagogies, I discovered that a case study format decenters the authority of the professor and, through Socratic questioning, empowers students to discover the answers for themselves. Case studies allow for a greater diversity of materials in the classroom without tokenizing non-white or nonclassical musical styles and their participants. More importantly, it teaches musicological inquiry and methods—skills that are often ignored in a lecture-based classroom. After implementing this new pedagogy, students now report far higher levels of engagement and better retention of materials, even though very few would call the class "entertaining."

What Is a Case Study?

Disciplines such as business, law, and medicine have been using case studies in the classroom for decades, and schools like the Harvard Business School have built their reputations on this approach. Cases in these disciplines are most often *problems* that require a *solution*. For example, in a business class, students may be given a narrative description of a company's history, its market evaluation, and an emerging challenge in the marketplace, and the case narrative will end with a statement of the problem or problems, such as: Should the owners sell the company? At what price? In class, the students will discuss and analyze the data provided in the case in order to make a decision. The professor guides the discussion by asking questions. Students identify the criteria on which a decision can be based, practice argumentation, and learn from the multiple different solutions and arguments provided by their peers. This combination of narrative storytelling and discussion is why case studies are so powerful in the classroom. Stories engage "a multitude of cognitive and affective mechanisms including perception, attention, memory, reasoning, simulation of actions, emotion, and, naturally, language."[3] In short, cases "help students learn how to think, plan, and reason."[4]

Despite the success of this approach in other disciplines, instructors in the humanities have been slow to use case studies in the classroom. In music history, three possible hurdles may be the cause for this reluctance. First, if case studies present problems that need solutions, it's not immediately clear what a musicological "problem" might be. Historical moments or artifacts do not present problems in the same way that a legal or business case might, and it's difficult to understand how a case study pedagogy might be adapted to study a past event that does not now nor in the near future require a decision or a solution. Case studies, however, can exercise other skills; as I discuss below, cases can also help students learn to create rich descriptions or make evaluations. These skills are more clearly musicological than problem solving and, as such, easier to implement in a music history classroom.

Second, until fairly recently, the study of subjects such as music and art history, literature, and even philosophy has centered on a more-or-less agreed upon pedagogical canon. To study music history without Brahms, art history without Rembrandt, or philosophy without Kant seems risible. And yet, as we all know, our survey courses routinely leave out art and artifacts from non-Western sources, women, and people of color. But we continue to see the survey course as "comprehensive" and value the "coverage" of the subject that it provides. To adopt a case study approach means sacrificing this "coverage" criterion. Of course, the idea of "coverage" is a myth and, like our sister fields in the humanities, musicologists are actively reevaluating the purpose and value of the canon. A case study approach to music history will certainly leave out some canonic composers and pieces—perhaps even Brahms!

Third, we may have trouble understanding how a case study approach helps us meet our current student learning outcomes (SLOs). For example, a survey of music history SLOs reveals that the many undergraduate music programs expect their students at the end of the music history sequence to be able to do the following:

1 Demonstrate knowledge of the principal eras, genres, composers, and instruments
2 Describe the distinct style periods, articulate the differences between styles, and aurally discriminate among styles

3   Recognize selected examples of Western music (visually and/or aurally)[5]

It might not be immediately clear how a case study approach can help music students learn how to remember facts, identify pieces, and recognize styles. I argue, however, that facts are not meaningful until they are properly contextualized, and students will not remember information that they do not need to immediately use. A case study approach certainly will not put as much information in front of a student as a lecture-based course; however, I have found that students *retain* far more information when studying cases than they do from hearing a lecture or taking a test. I also assert that it is odd that what we typically ask undergraduate students to do in the music history survey (memorize facts, or identify scores and recordings) has little to do with what we do as musicologists.

Music History Case Studies

The irony of our unfamiliarity with a case study pedagogical approach is that musicological research is almost always done from a case study perspective. We rarely produce quantitative studies; rather, we typically engage in close examinations of a single subject, or case. I argue that just as we scholars gather data about a single example in order to make a claim, assert an analysis, or compare or contrast the example to a similar one, students can learn to do the same in the classroom. Then, setting aside our preconceived ideas about what a music history course should do, let's ask ourselves, why not teach students to do in their own study of the discipline what we ourselves do as scholars? In other words, let's invite students to participate in musicological inquiry rather than give them facts and our own analyses.

Teaching musicological inquiry in the undergraduate classroom requires a radical rethinking of goals and outcomes. The SLOs for my own history courses are as follows:

At the end of the music history sequence, students should be able to do the following:

1   Demonstrate knowledge of cultural institutions and how they shape musical practices
2   Identify and describe significant stylistic features of a variety of musical practices throughout history
3   Engage in rigorous, open-minded, and creative inquiry regarding musical practices

4 Integrate multiple critical approaches to examine practical, artistic, and ethical issues related to music production and consumption
5 Locate, evaluate, and effectively use information to understand musical practices
6 Effectively express meaningful ideas about music in speech and writing

Note that the first two SLOs are very similar to the "standard" SLOs above. I do expect students to know something about style periods, composers, performers, and pieces. But more importantly, I expect them, in the process of engaging their own musicological inquiry, to go beyond knowing facts about historical musical styles to be able to evaluate and interrogate those facts. I want students to be able to ask a musicological question (SLO #3), examine the question from multiple perspectives (SLO #4), find and evaluate sources to answer the question (SLO #5), and communicate about the process (SLO #6).

A case study approach is an ideal way to teach musicological disciplinary practices, *in addition* to historical knowledge about music.

On the Use and Abuse of [Music] History

In his essay "Vom Nutzen und Nachteil der Historie für das Leben" (often translated as "On the Use and Abuse of History for Life"), Friedrich Nietzsche identifies three approaches to the study of history: the monumental, the antiquarian, and the critical.[6] These approaches respectively represent our human needs to revere, to conserve, and to challenge, and all three serve an important role, not only in the construction of history but also in the service of life.

The monumental approach best serves the one who longs to do or create something great and looks for models to emulate. The monumental approach is a celebration of great men (only occasionally women) and great works. The monumental celebrates *individuals* who struggle against limitations or experience conflict. Nietzsche claims that the celebration of lofty moments from the distant past can create faith in humanity—faith that we can overcome "the musty habit, the petty, and the menial," all that casts a "heavy atmosphere on everything great ... deceiving, dampening, and suffocating" those on the road to greatness.[7] If greatness was once there, says the student of the monumental, then it will be possible once again.

The one who approaches history as an antiquarian does so to emphasize the quotidian in order to conserve and honor it. In an antiquarian approach to history, everything is equally important and the focus is on the collective instead of the individual. Antiquarians do not assign value, as the monumental historian does; historical items are worthy of reverence simply because they are historical. According to Nietzsche, the antiquarian runs the risk of overvaluing the past (simply because it is past) and undervaluing what is new or innovative (simply because it is *not* the past). The antiquarian approach becomes a stumbling block for anything new because, according to Nietzsche, the antiquarian history "knows only how to preserve life, not how to create it."[8]

If the monumental serves the one who desires to act, and the antiquarian the one who desires to conserve and preserve, then the critical approach to history serves the one in need of emancipation from the limits of past histories. "A person must have the power, and from time to time must use it," according to Nietzsche, "to destroy a past and to dissolve it, in order to live." One does this "by taking the past to court, meticulously investigating it, and finally condemning it."[9] The critical approach seeks out injustices in the construction of past histories—both monumental and antiquarian. Nietzsche says that it is a dangerous process to judge the past in order to destroy it, because we are all products of earlier generations. When we judge history, we judge ourselves; it is "never possible to loose oneself from this chain entirely," even when the critical approach is necessary.[10]

It is easy to see these three approaches at play in music historical pedagogies: Most textbooks and accompanying anthologies present a monumental history, primarily through the lens of great composers and masterpiece compositions. Early music and performance practice studies adopt an antiquarian approach—conserving past knowledge and practices, not because they are "great" or better than others, but simply because they are part of our past. Critical approaches respond to the injustices of past music histories and are typically written from the point of view of those who have been excluded from the historical record.

Nietzsche's goal is historical study "in the service of life," which means that history must become a form of life, "an expression of life." How can each approach serve life? The monumental mode can provide the motivation to rise up out of one's present circumstances as a unique individual. The antiquarian mode can inspire a personal acquisition or integration of the past into oneself. The critical approach not only is destructive, but also has a "power to heal wounds, replace what has been lost, [and] to recreate the broken forms."[11] Nietzsche argues for all three approaches to history (alongside a healthy dose of "forgetfulness" or *unhistorical* thinking). Such an approach, he argues, can counteract the totalitarian and unjust tendencies of historical objectivity, which he calls a delusion, as well as a discomfort with the study of history as a leisure activity—a kind of conspicuous consumption of cultural capital. The study of a music-historical case can be done from any of the three approaches: a case may be an exploration of a musical monument or a primary source or an archival collection, or it may be a critique of past historical narratives. I readily admit that my approach leans heavily on the critical—even when centered on a musical monument or archival collection—as I find that students receive a healthy monumental and antiquarian point of view through other coursework and their ensembles. It may seem from my sample case studies that the object is primarily to politicize learning and to teach students, almost exclusively, to identify historical errors. My goal is much more expansive. I hope to teach my students how knowledge is constructed, and how in the process of that construction, injustices are perpetrated. If the critical approach focuses only on past wrongs, then the pedagogical objective becomes almost purely vindictive. However, the destruction of past "objective" histories can be *creative*, when they create more expansive historical understandings, and create new ways of relating the past to our current and future lives. The approach is also *healing* in the sense that it instills what Nietzsche describes as "a new habit, a new instinct, a new second nature."[12] We must balance a study of past injustices with practical steps for present and future healing.

For example, while studying, for example, Fanny Hensel and the systematic exclusion of women from the canon, it is all too easy to simply become angry about how women were and are excluded from the institutions and social circles that lead to prestige and success as a composer. But anger alone leads to rigid thinking, a narrowed vision, and is ultimately disempowering. Students desperately need to see themselves as *empowered* and capable of instilling change. They don't need us to supply them with more facts about music history; they need, rather, to know how to source their own knowledge, accurately contextualize and corroborate it, and use it to create new knowledge and practices. Natural outrage must be paired with hopeful action, and that is why we need a new, critical musicological pedagogy.

Types of Cases: Descriptive, Interpretive, and Evaluative

Cases in business, medicine, and law are designed to teach problem-solving and decision-making skills because practitioners in those fields must be able to make decisions in order to take proper action. Doctors have to be able to diagnose an illness and decide on a course of treatment. Sometimes, musicians need to be able to make historically informed decisions in order to take action (e.g., selecting proper ornamentation, knowing when one can or cannot ignore repeat signs, or making repertoire selections for a performance). But when we are working with historical materials, we are often in the business of describing, interpreting, and evaluating them. A decision that leads to action is not always necessary. I find that there is a natural scaffolding from descriptive, to interpretive, to evaluative cases; interpretive and evaluative cases require higher order critical thinking skills than descriptive ones.

While often not especially complex, descriptive cases are useful because they can illustrate a concept or context, or investigate historical constructs, theories, or analyses. The goal is that the students will come to not only *understand* something about the historical event or context at the end of the case but also *build* musicological skills in the process of acquiring such understanding. For example, a descriptive case might be "How do composers draw on conventional musical topics to create meaning?" Such a case demonstrates musical style elements of the Classical period and investigates how music might be meaningful to specific listeners and how that meaning is created and shared.

Interpretive cases might explore performance practice issues or problems in historical notations. Students must use analytical skills to interpret historical materials within present contexts. An interpretive case could be, "How was music used in the 2016 presidential campaign?" Using theories about cultural capital and the role of music in shaping group identity, an interpretive question could be, "How did the candidates use music to shape their campaigns and what political messages were the candidates trying to convey through music?"

Evaluative cases go beyond description and interpretation with a goal that students will learn to make critical *evaluations* of the case. In such cases, the case study narrative is a rich description of the *facts* of the event, but students in evaluative cases also provide their own analysis and evaluation of the case in the classroom. Such cases might engage an ethical perspective. For example, one might ask, "Should we continue to perform Mozart's *Don Giovanni* and, if so, how should we stage it?" Or, "Is Danger Mouse's *The Grey Album* a creative work or merely a mashup of the Beatles' *The White Album* and Jay-Z's *The Black Album*?" Such cases teach "critical approaches to examine practical, artistic, legal, and ethical issues related to music production and consumption," which is SLO #4 above.

Arguments for a Case Study Approach

Student Engagement

In my 2016 article "From Answers to Questions: Fostering Student Creativity and Engagement in Research and Writing," I compare students to buckets and ice cubes.[13] One fairly traditional educational philosophy assumes that the learner is like a bucket. Students start the educational process as empty buckets and the bits of knowledge we teach them are like chunks thrown into their buckets. We can measure the level in the bucket with tests or other types of assessments, and significant measuring points are celebrated with graduations and awards. This educational approach is based on a number of problematic assumptions. First, this model assumes that we are all more or less uniform learners who can acquire and retain knowledge and skills similarly. But what if the buckets are different sizes or are placed at different distances from the instructor? Second, by necessity, this model assumes that the bucket stays still. How can the teacher throw in the educational lumps if the bucket is fidgeting, interrupting, or asking questions?

Since the buckets are passive and uniform, the burden of success with this model is on the teacher. In his seminal work *Pedagogy of the Oppressed*, Paulo Freire calls this pedagogy the "banking" approach to education; similar in substance to the bucket analogy, he uses the metaphor that students are "bank accounts" and teachers make deposits into them. Freire claims that this system is "an instrument of dehumanization."[14] The bucket or banking pedagogical approach is designed to produce students who can regurgitate "objectively" correct answers and think in linear, information-based ways. A "bucket" pedagogy does not support the skills necessary to create independent, creative thinkers.

The social psychologist Kurt Lewin proposed an alternative model; instead of buckets, learners should be like ice cubes.[15] As learners, we often start the educational process with a predictable and stable mindset—hence the frozen cube. But then the ice cube moves toward a heat source, such as a candle, which in the metaphor is the educational process. As the ice cube gets close to the candle, part of it melts. This process is uncomfortable for most learners. It is a process of dismantling the existing mindset and recognizing that one has a shortcoming or a deficit to be corrected. For students who are comfortable with and thus may favor the bucket pedagogy, this process feels like losing ground. Most people find this period of ambiguity uncomfortable, and their reaction is to back away from the heat. The last stage of the process is that of "refreezing," as our new mindset crystallizes and the ambiguity abates. As we "refreeze," we never assume the old cube shape—instead, we assume an interesting, new, and slightly more complex shape. Initially, the ice cube is "pushed" toward the flame; that is, we push the students toward transformative change through required assignments and class meetings. But as all educators know, the student is in control of the transformation—not all come away from our classes changed.

Ideally, the students will become comfortable enough with the ambiguity of transformational change such that this process of "melting" and "refreezing" takes on its own momentum. After the initial push toward the flame, the cube returns again and again under its own motivation, continually transforming itself until it is a unique and complex creation. Similarly, Freire argues for "co-intentional education." He claims that teachers and students

> are both Subjects, not only in the task of unveiling ... reality, and thereby coming to know it critically, but in the task of re-creating ... knowledge. As they attain this knowledge of reality through common reflection and action, they discover themselves as its permanent re-creators.

Freire claims that this model is not one of "pseudo-participation, but committed involvement."[16]

I consider of course the lecture format classroom—in which the instructor is the primary actor and assessment is based on quizzes and tests—a "bucket" model of education. While the lecture-based survey may cover a good deal of content, it fails to inspire the students to share their gifts in the classroom. A case study approach, in contrast, requires active participation from students and instructors alike and recognizes that students bring a considerable amount of skill and knowledge to the classroom. Moreover, the discussion-based inquiry that a case study approach facilitates empowers students to learn from each other and to look to each other (and themselves) for affirmation instead of always looking to the instructor.

The discomfort of "melting" and "refreezing" creates an ideal condition for learning, and, accordingly, it is the cases with gray areas—areas of ambiguity—that provide the richest conditions for learning. In 1908, psychologists Robert Yerkes and John Dillingham Dodson published a study that finds that human performance increases as emotional arousal or stress increases. According to Yerkes and Dodson, people can perform simple tasks at peak performance even in very high-stress

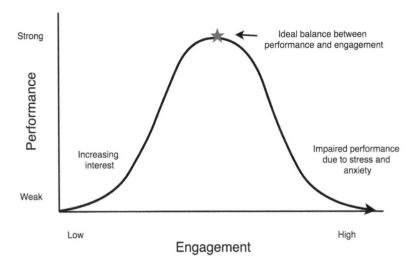

Figure 1.1 Yerkes-Dodson Law.[17]

environments, but for sophisticated tasks, as stress increases performance drops, as shown in Figure 1.1.

As students work through a case in the classroom, the instructor resists providing answers outright and instead pushes the students for greater detail or deeper analysis. The goal is for the students to maintain peak performance by engaging ambiguity, even when it may be frustrating for them. It is not uncommon for students during this process to express all kinds of emotions—frustration, anger, or joy. The emotional element is an important factor in what instructional design expert Dee Fink describes as "significant learning." "When students care about something," according to Fink, "they then have the *energy* they need for learning more about it and making it a part of their lives. Without the energy for learning, nothing significant happens."[18] Chapter 4 provides a detailed discussion of how to guide classroom discussion and find an appropriate level of emotional engagement that allows students to perform at their best.

Higher-Order Learning

The primary benefit of a case study pedagogy for students is that it compels them to exercise higher order learning skills. In 1956, educational psychologist Benjamin Bloom and his collaborators created a framework to describe learning, called Bloom's Taxonomy.[19] Despite the schema's ubiquity in faculty-development literature, it is often critiqued as inappropriately hierarchical, overly prescriptive, and difficult to interpret and apply.[20] The taxonomy is usually represented as a pyramid, with "remembering" as the broad base and "creating" as the tiny top of the pyramid. I find it more useful to think of the taxonomy as a wedge, as in Figure 1.2, with "remember," "understand," and "apply" as essential foundational skills, and "synthesize" "evaluate," and "analyze" as higher-order skills.

In spite of its limitations, the taxonomy nonetheless serves as a useful frame for thinking about desired student outcomes. The taxonomy challenges us to think beyond what we want students to know, and what skills we would like them to have as a result of their studies. When working on a case, students are engaging most of the taxonomy: learning the "facts" of the case, or locating and describing information; summarizing, interpreting, and discussing the facts in small groups or in class; and then analyzing and evaluating, which involves exploring relationships and making judgments. Ideally, the case study culminates in creative work as students formulate their own research questions for further inquiry. Ideally, these projects engage one of the two upper wings of the taxonomy by either synthesizing information in order to

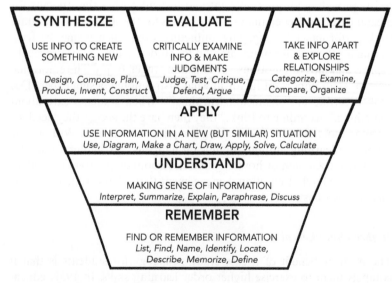

Figure 1.2 Bloom's Taxonomy.[21]

create something new or by taking apart the information in order to make a deep analysis.

Diversity and Inclusion

In 2016, the College Music Society's Undergraduate Music Major Taskforce published a manifesto calling for change, and diversity was one of three core pillars for reform, alongside creativity and integration. The report identifies the "ethnocentric orientation of music studies," as a serious deficiency that "carries enormous societal ramifications." The authors claim that "Once rectified, the resulting change opens important avenues of learning."[22] The sample cases I mention above (Hensel, presidential campaign music, and Danger Mouse) include styles, creators, and constituencies that are underrepresented in the canon of Western music and the traditional music history curriculum. In a case study analysis, even one of the most iconic masterpieces—Mozart's *Don Giovanni*— requires a more critical, inclusive, and diverse point of view. Asking students to evaluate the ethical dilemmas of staging the opera requires them to do more than learn about the piece and its compositional context; it asks them to take account of the lived experience of the piece, then and now. The value of a case study isn't in its content *per se*, but rather in the critical discussion and creative inquiry it can inspire.

This realignment of educational priorities requires a fundamental shift in thinking about the centrality of content, which in turn helps blur hierarchical binaries such as high/low, Western/Other, mind/body, and professional/amateur. Because a case requires that we meet it on its own terms, diverse musical examples—especially ones that lack traditional notation or are distributed and consumed in a unique way—appear much less tokenistic than they often do when included in a traditional anthology of Western music. And if we want to take Nietzsche's provocation that history should serve life, then we should create cases that address local musical practices and communities. Such studies could easily draw on local scenes, traditions, and archival collections.

Universal Design

In addition to creating a more diverse and engaging educational experience, a case study pedagogy can accommodate a much wider array of learners than traditional pedagogies do. In a lecture/test class, students often struggle against learning deficits, especially attention, recall, and anxiety. In a case study class, students work collectively using their strengths. Universal Design for Learning (UDL) is a framework that recognizes diverse ways of learning and attempts to remove barriers for learning.[23] Typical barriers to success in a lecture class may include the emphasis on testing as the primary assessment tool and a lack of engagement for a number of reasons, including lack of representation in the curriculum.

A course designed according to UDL principles minimizes barriers to learning, recognizing that students have a wide variety of backgrounds, strengths, needs, and interests. The case study classroom accommodates all students by radically shifting the burden of learning from the individual to the group. Small groups can be used for pre-case preparation and post-case creative inquiry and research. The large class works collectively to examine, analyze, and evaluate cases, and the collective nature of the educational experience is a key tenet of UDL. According to the authors of *Universal Design for Learning: Theory and Practice*, this approach serves the class holistically. They write:

> It's not only the individual student that benefits from UDL, but the totality of learners that make up the learning environment, which, in turn, can be an environment of expert learners only when all students are actively involved in creating knowledge and establishing its value.[24]

A UDL classroom recognizes the value of every student and the gifts that they bring to the learning environment. "In other words," they claim, "the learning environment itself is impacted by the engagement and progress of each learner."[25]

How to Use This Book

This book is designed for teachers interested in learning more about how to integrate case studies into their pedagogical toolkit. While the examples in this book are largely from music history classes for music majors, these practices can be applied to a wide variety of class types and used with diverse groups of students—majors and nonmajors, as well as undergraduate and graduate students.

In Chapter 2, I challenge the traditional "coverage" model of the music history survey and describe how to design, as a replacement, a curriculum based on case studies. I also offer advice on how to integrate cases into more traditional, lecture-based classrooms.

In Chapter 3, I give detailed information on how to find and write cases. It is difficult to find materials that hit what I call the "sweet spot" for undergraduates—that is, materials that are rich enough to inspire a fruitful discussion, but not so challenging that students can't grasp the content. I guide the reader here to open access materials, blogs, podcasts, and long-form journalism that can serve as excellent starting points for a case study; I explain how to write your own case studies for your students; and I demonstrate how to guide students through more difficult materials in order to help them prepare for a case study discussion before they enter the classroom.

Chapter 4 explores preparing and leading a case study discussion. I focus here on how to guide students through course materials with questions rather than lectures. This chapter includes examples from my own classroom discussions that demonstrate how to pose questions that will inspire discussion.

In Chapter 5, I discuss how to leverage small group work for inquiry and research. Cases provide an excellent starting point for further inquiry and for problem-based learning strategies. I give examples of group work projects and discuss how to mentor groups, especially those in conflict.

In Chapter 6, I discuss assessment practices for both class discussion and group work. I suggest ways to grade class participation and ways to support students with accommodations, especially those with social anxiety.

Stepping Out of the Limelight

It was difficult for me at first to let go of the lecture format. Many of us come from performance backgrounds and enjoy the "song and dance" aspect of a well-crafted lecture. I was good at it, and I missed having a captive audience that actively listens to what I'm telling them and laughs at my jokes. There was also something wonderful about introducing students to a piece that I had known intimately for years, sometimes decades, and leading them through the details of its twists and turns. Letting go of this beloved content was a struggle. But trading my classroom "performances" for true transformational change in the students has been in the end an easy one to make. The experience of learning alongside and from the students as they develop and exercise nascent musicological skills has proven to be far more satisfying both for me and, as evidence has shown, my students.

Notes

1 Mark Edmundson, "On the Uses of a Liberal Education: I. As Lite Entertainment for Bored College Students," *Harper's Magazine*, September, 1997, 40.

2 Madeline St. Amour, "What Happens Before College Matters," *Inside Higher Ed,* October 20, 2020, www.insidehighered.com/news/2020/10/20/black-students-need-changes-policies-and-structures-beyond-higher-education

3 Moritz Lehne, Philipp Engel, Martin Rohrmeier, Winfried Menninghaus, Arthur M. Jacobs, and Stefan Koelsch, "Reading a Suspenseful Literary Text Activates Brain Areas Related to Social Cognition and Predictive Inference," *Plos One,* May 6, 2015, https://doi.org/10.1371/journal.pone.0124550

4 William Naumes and Margaret J. Naumes, *The Art and Craft of Case Writing,* 2nd ed. (New York: M. E. Sharpe, 2006), 5.

5 This survey was based on widely available web-based materials. A more systematic and thorough survey of music history program SLOs is much needed.

6 Friedrich Nietzsche, "Vom Nutzen und Nachteil der Histories für das Leben," *Unzeitgemäße Betrachtungen* (reprint Berlin: Holzinger, 2014), 209–285. All translations are the author's.

7 Nietzsche, "Vom Nutzen," 219.

8 Nietzsche, 227.

9 Nietzsche, 228.

10 Nietzsche, 229–230.

11 Nietzsche, 212.

12 Nietzsche, 229.

13 Sara Haefeli, "From Answers to Questions: Fostering Student Creativity and Engagement in Research and Writing," *Journal of Music History Pedagogy* 7, no. 1 (2016): 1–17. The following paragraphs are an adaptation of material on pp. 5–6.

14 Paulo Freire, *Pedagogy of the Oppressed,* trans. Myra Bergman Ramos (New York: Continuum, 1970), 54.

15 See Edgar H. Schein, "Kurt Lewin's Change Theory in the Field and in the Classroom: Notes toward a Model of Managed Learning," *Systems Practice* 9, no. 1 (1996): 27–47.

16 Freire, *Pedagogy of the Oppressed,* 69.

17 Based on the diagram in David M. Diamond, Adam M. Campbell, Collin R. Park, Joshua Halonen, and Phillip R. Zoladz, "The Temporal Dynamics Model of Emotional Memory Processing: A Synthesis on the Neurobiological Basis of Stress-Induced Amnesia, Flashbulb and Traumatic Memories, and the Yerkes-Dodson Law," *Neural Plasticity* 33 (2007), doi:10.1155/2007/60803

18 Dee Fink, "What Is 'Significant Learning?'" PDF, accessed April 14, 2020, www.wcu.edu/WebFiles/PDFs/facultycenter_SignificantLearning.pdf

19 Benjamin Bloom, *Taxonomy of Educational Objectives: The Classification of Educational Goals* (New York: Longmans, Green, & Co., 1956). See also Lorin W. Anderson and David R. Krathwohl, *A Taxonomy for Learning, Teaching, and Assessing: A Revision of Bloom's Taxonomy of Educational Objectives* (New York: Longman, Inc. 2001).

20 For further criticisms, see Seyyed Mohammad Ali Soozandehfar and Mohammad Reza Adeli, "A Critical Appraisal of Bloom's Taxonomy,"

American Research Journal of English and Literature 2 (2016), www.arjonl ine.org/papers/arjel/v2-i1/14.pdf

21 Adapted from The Derek Bok Center for Teaching and Learning, "Taxonomies of Learning," *Harvard University,* accessed April 14, 2020, https://bokcenter.harvard.edu/taxonomies-learning

22 "Transforming Music Study from Its Foundations: A Manifesto for Progressive Change in the Undergraduate Preparation of Music Majors," College Music Society, January 2016, www.music.org/pdf/pubs/tfumm/ TFUMM.pdf

23 See Anne Meyer, David Rose, and David Gordon, *Universal Design for Learning: Theory and Practice* (Wakefield, MA: CAST Professional Publishing, 2014).

24 Meyer, Rose, and Gordon, *Universal Design for Learning,* 12.

25 Meyer, Rose, and Gordon, *Universal Design for Learning*, 12.

2   Case Study Curriculum Design

Imagine a course unit focused on the question, How does music create meaning? The unit unfolds in the second semester of a three-semester sequence of music history courses that are required for music majors. The students are mostly sophomores. We begin the unit by listening to Radiohead's "Everything in its Right Place," a song that clearly conveys—in opposition to its lyrics—that everything is *not* in its right place.[1] We then attempt to unpack how it is that we get this message from the song. One student notes the glitchy, fidgety digitized vocal line; another notes that the song is in the unsettling Phrygian mode; a third suggests that it is the odd meter that keeps us from finding a resting place, despite the incessant ground-bass repetitions; a fourth adds that the way sounds float and move around the virtual soundstage is otherworldly. Collectively, the students draw on their various strengths to explore what is happening with the song to create meaning.

The case study proper begins when students read Chapter One "From Rhetoric to Semiotics" of Stephen Rumph's book *Mozart and Enlightenment Semiotics*.[2] In the next class meeting, we discuss how music can convey meaning in Cherubino's aria "Non so più cosa son, cosa faccio" and the "Lacrimosa" movement of the *Requiem*. The students discover through their own dialogue and analysis how composers such as Mozart drew "upon a lexicon of conventional signs through which characters could communicate their emotions and desires," as Rumph asserts in the reading.[3] They also make connections to other pieces they know that use the same conventions, ranging from the bugle call-like opening of Beethoven's Symphony No. 3 to the fanfare in Lil Nas X and Jack Harlow's 2021 song "Industry Baby." The students are active, engaged, thinking creatively, critically, and analytically, and they are learning from each other and from the materials presented to them as the case study unfolds.

DOI: 10.4324/9781003130482-2

The success of a case study like the one described above depends on two factors: (1) how well the whole course is designed in advance and (2) how well the instructor can encourage and guide class discussions. This chapter addresses issues related to curriculum and course design. It may sound like a truism to say that good course design is essential, but for a case method class, as opposed to a lecture-based one, planning is even more important. It's a lot of work to create a new case-based course or to change a lecture-based course to one that uses case studies, but after this work is done, the effort during the semester will feel much lighter as the burden of downloading information into the students is lifted.

In this chapter, I give three different approaches to designing a case study curriculum that recognize a variety of levels of commitment to the method. I discuss a course design process that moves from defining overarching student learning outcomes, to defining course objectives, to selecting topics for cases, and finally to finding artifacts that will serve as the focus of each case study. I offer tips on how to write a syllabus for a case study class, arguing that the syllabus should serve as an invitation to learning, not as a legal contract. Finally, I discuss the difficulty of changing the culture that often exists in schools of music, conservatories, and other music programs, a culture that all too often is resistant to pedagogical and curricular innovation.

Finding a Balance between Coverage and Inquiry

Adopting a case study pedagogy is a sea change. It need not be made in one fell swoop; instead of diving into the depths, you can choose to wade in slowly. I suggest here, representing my own path, three possible approaches that move from small- to large-scale changes and which may be adopted incrementally:

Option 1: Change Just a Few Class Periods to Case Studies

My first foray into teaching cases entailed adding three case studies to a typical lecture-based survey of music after 1900. I presented the three cases with provocative questions:

- "Why are there no great women composers?"
- "Where are the musicians of color?"
- "How do avant garde and experimental composers make money?"[4]

For each case study, the students read an article, discussed it in class, and then in groups of five embarked on a directed research project. At the end of class, each group gave a two-minute presentation on what they learned. Each class period was fast-paced, and the students were active throughout. It seemed at first impossible to discuss an article, undertake a quick research project, and present findings in a 50-minute class period, but they did it. Over the course of the hour, spirited discussions moved from the whole class to small groups and back to the whole class. Students had their laptops out—not because they were distracting themselves—but because they were searching for information, evidence, or examples to share with the class. The presentations were extremely short yet packed with information. My role was to ask questions and keep the time, and I found that the hour flew by. Harkening back to Parini's terminology, it was *wild*.

For the case on women composers, the class read and discussed Marcia Citron's article "Gender, Professionalism, and the Canon." In this article, Citron scrutinizes the systematic exclusion of women from the canon, recognizing that women have faced significant barriers not only to a professional music education, but to the social circles that lead to publications, performances, and critical reception. During class discussion, students articulated the thesis of the article and explored some of the examples of women composers that Citron offers such as Cécile Chaminade and Fanny Hensel. They discussed specific language from the article that othered or excluded women and shared quotations whose exclusionary connotations angered them.[5]

After the large-group discussion, I sectioned the students into groups and gave each the name of a woman composer to research. Coincidentally, one of the groups consisted of five young men, most of whom were music composition majors, and when they were randomly given Yoko Ono, one of them groaned, "She's *the worst*." It's impossible to say if the groan was inspired by Ono's experimental conceptualism or by her putative role in the Beatles' breakup. I suggested that perhaps they were repeating what they had heard about her and that they might not really know her work. One of the students admitted, to my surprise, that I was right—he *didn't* really know much about her work. As they started reading about Ono, they noticed how her husbands, Toshi Ichiyanagi and John Lennon, overshadow her in the literature—even in biographies ostensibly about her—and that the Wikipedia article on Ono was more about Lennon and the Beatles than it was about her.[6] They saw firsthand what Citron had described in the article, namely, language that dismissed and othered her. Their experience did indeed encourage a skepticism of received knowledge, and as they explored performances of Ono's works, they made new connections between evidence in the historical record and their lived experiences as musicians.

During the class devoted to the question of how experimental composers made money, students had to think creatively about how to answer the question. They discovered that some composers, like Milton Babbitt, were university professors and that if they looked at public salary records they could guess what his annual income might have been. They also knew from his biography that he won numerous prizes that included large cash awards. Students discovered that other composers, such as Meredith Monk, had created nonprofit foundations to support themselves and their work. They also learned that some composers like Julius Eastman struggled to make ends meet and that Eastman was essentially homeless toward the end of his life. The overarching takeaway was that it was very difficult to find evidence of commissions and other sources of income, which led to a conversation about why it is that we don't seem want to connect the arts to financial concerns in the United States.

These examples demonstrate that it is fairly easy to replace just a few lectures with a case study—without the pain of giving up coverage. If you are hesitant to give up the survey, try replacing some of your lectures with a case. The cases can address large-scale epistemological issues and critical biases (as the examples above) or they can explore a specific musical phenomenon or event in close detail. Students can prepare for the case by reading an article, listening to a podcast, watching a video, or studying a performance and/or score. The important thing is that the case unfolds in the classroom through directed questions (as discussed in Chapter 4). Ideally, discussion of the case will be followed by further inquiry and research (as discussed in Chapter 5).

Option 2: Change the Class

These first dips in the case studies pool were so exciting and effective that I decided to stop lecturing altogether in future courses and use only cases. As described in Chapter 1, the goal was to diversify the content of the course, to make it more engaging, and to make it more accessible for all learners. I had become convinced that continuing to teach the narrow and exclusive history of "the canon" was harming my students, but the classes in the course catalog were still survey courses: Music History I–III divided into historical periods: I. Medieval, Renaissance, and Baroque; II. Classical and Romantic; and III. Music After 1900.

If I abandoned the canon—and along with it my lectures, tests, textbooks, and anthologies—I had to rethink what I was to teach. But

I was also convinced by my case study experiences that the issue wasn't just *what* I was supposed to teach, but *how* I was to teach it. Without naming it as such, I adopted a "backwards design" approach to the class.[7] The frame for the course stayed the same, but I reconsidered my learning outcomes: What did I want my students to know and be able to do at the end of the survey? Did I want them to be able to label, define, identify, and remember? Or did I want them to be able to describe, explain, analyze, synthesize, and create? Of course I wanted them to be operating in the upper levels of Bloom's taxonomy.

As discussed in Chapter 1, I revised my learning outcomes to include skills that enable students to *do* music history: to inquire, think critically, locate and use sources, and argue. Once I recognized that lectures and tests were not helpful in either meeting or demonstrating these outcomes, it was easy to give up on lecturing and to adopt a case study approach. As I selected cases, I chose ones that simultaneously had "content" that I think is important (facts are indeed important) and, more significantly, are rich with ambiguity, controversy, or mystery. The cases I selected were designed to inspire further inquiry, and I could measure success not by the content students could recite, but by the quality of the questions they could generate.

Table 2.1 lists the case topics and preparatory assignment for the third semester of our survey—Music History After 1900.

Table 2.1 Outline of case study topics and preparatory assignments

Case Study	Preparatory Assignment
Beyoncé's *Lemonade*	Robin James, "How Not to Listen to *Lemonade: Music Criticism and Epistemic Violence*"[8]
Stravinsky's *Rite of Spring*	Tamara Levitz, "Racism at The Rite"[9]
"Entartete Musik" ["Degenerate Music"]	Watch: "Art as Propaganda: The Nazi Degenerate Art Exhibit"[10] Read: "The Nazis' take on 'Degenerate Music'"[11]
Lincoln Center, the Arts, and Gentrification	Julia Foulkes, "Streets and Stages: Urban Renewal and the Arts After World War II"[12]
Experimentalism & the Art Ensemble of Chicago	John Cage, "Experimental Music," from *Silence*,[13] and Paul Steinbeck, "Introduction" to *Message to Our Folks*.[14]
Camp Aesthetics	Mattijs van de Port, "Genuinely Made Up: Camp, Baroque, and Other Denaturalizing Aesthetics and the Cultural Production of the Real"[15]

While the ordering happens to be chronological (*after* the first case), it is meant to step the students through a progression of diverse skills. The cases move from individual works, to a bounded time period, to a style, to a location/venue, and finally to a broad aesthetic. Cases should involve increasingly greater ambiguity or complexity as the course proceeds, which allows for better, deeper inquiry as the students get more skilled at asking musicological questions.

Option 3: Change the Curriculum

After my first forays with cases (first employing just a few, and then replacing lectures with cases), I found it necessary to rethink the curricular frame altogether. I was motivated to reimagine our traditional curricular requirements because I found that trying to introduce greater diversity into the existing survey tokenized the diverse examples. The problem wasn't the cases, but the chronological frame that implied a teleological, iterative study of style periods, genres, (genius) composers, and (master)pieces. Chronology tends to suggest that musical discoveries are like those in the natural sciences and that composers build upon the musical discoveries of their predecessors. The problem with this construct, of course, is that we can't study musics that don't participate in this march of progress without tokenizing them.

Large-scale curriculum change requires departmental collaboration, and my colleagues and I decided to reframe the study of music within its lived contexts. We were guided by the notion of a "Usable Past," that is, an exploration of our musical history that helps us understand who we are as musicians, what we have done, and what we might create as a musical future.[16] We called the courses "Music in Context" and identified six such contexts: the Academy, the Temple, the Palace, the Stage, the Home, and the Marketplace. Instead of focusing on composers and pieces, this frame suggests that performers, audiences, patrons, inventors, and technologies have shaped musical practices just as strongly as composers have. Case studies within this frame demonstrate the constructedness of any single historical narrative and encourage students to be active participants in the making of this record. A primary virtue of the focus on contextual music making practices is that it acts as a shortcut for students who desire to see themselves in the historical record. We recognize that music history is non-monolithic, and thus our modular approach with institutions as an organizing schema serves as just one way to tell the story of music history. (See Appendix 1 for other sample course schedules.)

Other instructors have organized their courses around key musicological questions or problems:

• How do power and patronage shape musical style?
• How are performance and pedagogical canons created, and why are
  some people systematically excluded from the canon?
• How is it possible to commodify music? How has music been
  marketed and consumed?
• What is notation? How have musicians communicated musical
  ideas in the past? What does notation actually say, and what does it
  fail to communicate?
• What is improvisation? How does it disrupt traditional notation
  practices and introduce a different vision of music creation? How
  have musicians engaged in real-time music creation in the past?
• How does music carry and create meaning? How does it create
  identity?

Musicologist John Spilker employs themes such as "Gender and
Sexuality" and "The Environment" to juxtapose canonic examples
from the past and recent musical examples.[17] For example, in Spilker's
class "Music History I: Gender & Sexualities," he juxtaposes medieval
troubaritz song and the blues to draw out themes of complaint and pro-
test; a case study on the madrigal and rap invites a discussion of coded
discourse on sexualities; and a study of baroque opera and songs for
drag performances highlight the performative nature of gender.[18]

Until recently, a common assumption was that music history was
best taught by way of a chronological survey of the Western canon. The
solution to the problem of the canonic survey cannot be yet another
grand narrative. Rather, solutions must be diverse, each reflecting its
particular context. Spilker's solution suits his own strengths as a scholar
as well as the needs of his students and those of his institution. Instead
of simply mimicking another instructor's model, I invite you to create
a solution that follows the mission of your own institution, the needs
of your own student body, and the nature and breadth of your own
interests. For example, musicologist Trudi Wright teaches at Regis
College in a small music program. The size of the program has inspired
Wright and her colleagues to closely tie the content of the music history courses to their concert programming. Regis is a Jesuit institution
guided by the mission of *cura personalis*, or, care for the whole person,
and Wright has created a pedagogy of care as a foundation for all of her
classes.[19] Harvard is a very different institution, and their controversial
2017 curriculum changes that eliminated typical core requirements in

music history and theory were made, according to professor Suzannah Clark, partially in response to the "intellectual and academic climate of the study of music generally." Far more importantly, however, these curricular decisions are, as Clark put it, "a reflection of our faculty, and a reflection of our current students."[20]

Course Design Process

Once you have defined the program-level SLOs, you should (1) create course-specific SLOs, (2) define course objectives, (3) choose the topics of the case studies, and (4) select the preparatory artifacts (reading, listening, viewing assignments). I often swap steps 3 and 4, as a great article or artifact can inspire the study of a case.

Steps 1 and 2

While a great article or artifact will often inspire a case study, not every intriguing or novel piece of scholarship will support the desired learning outcomes. The course-specific student learning outcomes act as a plumb line by which one can measure the suitability of a case. When my colleagues and I redesigned our curriculum, we wanted to do more than simply rearrange or diversify the content; we wanted to encourage emerging expertise in the students.

We've already talked about creating SLOs; here it is important to distinguish between SLOs (step 1) and course objectives (step 2). SLOs describe the knowledge and skills that students will have *after* the course is completed, whereas course objectives are the topics, exercises, and assignments covered *during* the class. Instructors often confuse the two. Student learning outcomes answer the question, What do I want my students to be able to do at the end of the semester? Course objectives answer the question, What will the students be doing in the classroom or during the course of the semester? Course objectives are the specific activities and subjects of study that support acquisition of the SLOs. Table 2.2 demonstrates the differences between objectives and outcomes with concrete examples.

The course objectives in Table 2.2 are typical musical historical activities, but may not apply to a case-based study of music in a historical context. To create your own student learning outcomes, take into account your larger learning goals as well as the classroom activities. Start each student learning outcome with the phrase "Students will be able to …" Follow up with an action verb (in italics in Table 2.2). The

Table 2.2 Relationship between course objectives and student learning
outcomes

Course Objectives	Student Learning Outcomes
*Describes what students will do **during** the class*	*Describes knowledge and skills students will have **after the class***
Students will *study* major stylistic periods, composers, performers, genres, and pieces.	Students will be able to *identify* major stylistic periods, composers, performers, genres, and pieces.
Students will *read* and *discuss* primary and secondary sources on a variety of historical music-making practices.	Students will be able to *summarize* and *explain* academic writing. Students will be able to *formulate* a defense and/or critique in response to a scholarly argument.
Students will *write* a research paper using a variety of sources and source types.	Students will be able to *find* and *assess* scholarly sources, *create* a research question, and *communicate* effectively about music.

action verb indicates how students will demonstrate their ability; for
example, students will demonstrate an ability to communicate effectively about music through speech and/or writing. "Understand" is a
poor action verb because it does not indicate how students will demonstrate understanding.

Bloom's taxonomy for learning can be useful here to help identify the
level of learning. Introductory courses may focus more on foundational
skills such as remembering, understanding, and applying; upper-level
and graduate courses will likely promote high-order skills such as analyzing, evaluating, and synthesizing. The list of action verbs associated
with each level shown in Table 2.3 is especially helpful when creating
student learning outcomes.

Steps 3 and 4

As you start to select cases, keep in mind that the first case will set
the tone for the semester, and the last one should be as comprehensive as possible, so that students can apply the knowledge and skills
they've learned from previous cases. To begin each case, students start
with an artifact—such as a scholarly article, primary source reading, or
performance—and answer a set of questions that help them evaluate and
understand the resource. As you select artifacts, aim for the following:

1   a variety of author/creator identities
2   a mix of both primary and secondary source readings

Table 2.3 Using Bloom's Taxonomy and action verbs to create student learning
outcomes[21]

Bloom's Level	Action Verbs	Example Learning Outcome
Remember	list, recite, outline, define, name, match, quote, recall, identify, label, recognize	Students will be able to name the major jazz styles of the twentieth century.
Understand	describe, explain, paraphrase, restate, give original examples of, summarize, contrast, interpret, discuss.	Students will be able to describe each style period and provide examples.
Apply	calculate, predict, apply, solve, illustrate, use, demonstrate, determine, model, perform, operate, employ, sketch, present	Students will be able to demonstrate basic jazz and blues changes on an instrument of their choice.
Analyze	classify, break down, differentiate, distinguish, categorize, analyze, diagram, illustrate, associate	Students will be able to differentiate between scholarly and popular jazz publications.
Evaluate	choose, support, relate, determine, defend, judge, grade, compare, contrast, argue, justify, support, evaluate, assess	Students will be able to assess legal and financial practices associated with the commercial recording and distribution of jazz.
Synthesize	design, formulate, build, invent, create, compose, generate, derive, modify, develop, plan, write	Students will be able to formulate a research question and design a project.

3   a balance of difficult and accessible content
4   a variety of media types (reading, listening, viewing)

In past iterations of my Music History After 1900 class, the students
started the semester by reading Robin James's book chapter entitled
"How Not to Listen to *Lemonade*: Music Criticism and Epistemic
Violence." We started the semester with Beyoncé's *Lemonade* album
because James argues for the kind of discipline-specific research
I wanted the students to be engaging in for the rest of the semester. The
chapter addresses issues of white supremacy and male privilege in historical and analytical research, and her research question is, How can we
study music created by marginalized musicians without using violently
inappropriate epistemic frames, frames that privilege classical forms,

notation-based practices, and concert hall aesthetics. With respect to James's study of *Lemonade*, her concern was especially with how we separate "the music" from its context.[22] The article motivates students to explore Beyoncé's work within the various musical styles and contexts in which she is working. The next case in that course, Stravinsky's *Rite of Spring*, builds on skills gained in studying *Lemonade*, as it addresses similar issues connected to how scholars often define music *away* from its lived, embodied contexts, and how music is—more often than not— heard and experienced in racialized frames.

My inclusion of *Lemonade* here isn't to argue that it should be part of a pedagogical canon; it is to argue that we no longer need canons. The *Lemonade* example illustrates how I selected the topic and reading assignment in light of my desired learning outcomes and course objectives for the semester. The case fulfilled several goals for my Music History After 1900 class:

* It focuses on a significant artist from a marginalized community.
* The James book chapter addresses issues of canonization and bias inherent in music history and analysis.
* It demonstrates how important musicological inquiry is for critical analysis and evaluation.

The specific content of a case is less important than the skills it can help develop, and I do not teach the same cases for each iteration of the course. I stated above that giving up coverage and leaving out content is often difficult, but it is easier once you shift your selection criteria from *content* to *skills*. After identifying SLOs and course content, and after choosing the cases and preparatory assignments, you are ready to write the syllabus.

The Syllabus as an Invitation to a Case Study Approach

Since case studies will be unfamiliar to most music students, I find it useful to explain the methodology in the syllabus:

Case Method Pedagogy

What does it mean to study music history using case studies? A case method pedagogy uses narratives about specific moments in time to develop critical skills. This class is not a comprehensive study of a subject. Instead of listening to lectures about musical styles, composers, and pieces, you will be actively participating in the creation of knowledge through inquiry and research related to each case.

We will begin each case with a reading, listening, or viewing assignment and a discussion forum assignment on the on-line course management system. We will discuss each case in class. You will then work with your group to develop a research question and to complete a project.

I consider a syllabus to be an invitation to learning, and being explicit about the pedagogical approach clarifies and enlivens the invitation.

Invitations often clarify expectations (about how to dress, or whether to bring a gift), but they rarely include rules. I used to include "class policies" in the syllabus with statements such as

- No late assignments or makeup exams for unexcused absences.
- No email or phone discussions of grades as per privacy rights.
- Class disruptions (talking, cell phones, use of personal computer), leaving class early, and excessive lateness will lower your final grade.

These rules are not inviting; indeed, they indicate to students that I expect such negative behaviors and have to proactively guard against them. Even reframing the policies in positive terms (e.g., "show up on time and prepared," "stay attentive in class") is not much better. It still broadcasts to the students that I don't trust them.

With the shift from an instructor-focused and grading-heavy pedagogy to a student-centered one, I created a music history "bill of rights and corresponding responsibilities":

- You have a right to *a learning environment that ensures mental and physical wellness.*
- You have a right to *respect.*
- You have a right to *be assessed and graded fairly.*
- You have a right to *freedom of opinion and expression.*
- You have a right to *privacy and confidentiality.*
- You have a right to *meaningful and equal participation, to self-organize groups to improve your learning environment.*
- You have a right to *learn in an environment that is welcoming to all people. No student shall be isolated, excluded, or diminished in any way.*

While my role as instructor is important, it is also limited. With these rights come responsibilities:

• You are responsible for taking care of yourself, managing your time, and communicating with me and with others if things start to feel out of control or overwhelming.
• You have the responsibility of acting in a way that is worthy of respect and always respectful of others.
• Your experience with this course is directly related to the quality of the energy that you bring to it, and your energy shapes the quality of your peers' experiences.
• You are responsible for creating an inclusive environment and for speaking up when someone is excluded.

I have found that the bill of rights and responsibilities has helped create a classroom atmosphere that doesn't need to be ruled by punitive policies. A good invitation helps a person imagine themselves at the event, helps them fit in, and encourages them to feel comfortable in their own skin. The syllabus is an ideal opportunity to describe the learning community you wish to foster in your courses.

Changing the Culture

What to do in a situation where case study teaching is not the norm? Opposition may come from both colleagues and students. When I began teaching with cases, I was fortunate to have the support of my colleagues. However, I did face opposition from some students who were unsure that a case study approach would prepare them adequately for either graduate entrance or teaching certification exams. Some students felt that if they weren't taught the canon they wouldn't be able to keep up with their peers from the top-tier music conservatories. I also had students say that they learn better from lectures and tests. It helps to share with such students that future employers care more about critical thinking, creative problem solving, and analytical skills than about what facts they know. These comments typically come at the beginning of the semester before students experience the benefits of the case study approach and its challenges and rewards.

Changing the academic culture takes time and commitment. Epsen Andersen and Bill Schiano, authors of *Teaching with Cases: A Practical Guide*, suggest that addressing the culture should be part of your course preparation. This may mean that you need to prepare your colleagues as well as your students. This preparation should include:

- Making the content and message of the course clear to yourself and others.
- Ensuring that you have the authority and self-confidence to take control of the whole student experience.
- Understanding where your support and your opposition will be.
- Setting the students' expectations about the content and conduct of the course, and their own role in it.[23]

Andersen and Schiano also suggest communicating with your peers, department chairs, and administrators as much as possible. You might need to reach outside of your own department to find like-minded instructors, and perhaps your faculty development office may be a good resource. If you are a junior faculty member and are worried that such a pedagogical change could reflect poorly on your tenure application, have a frank discussion about the issue with your chair, director, or dean. I suspect that if your research and scholarship are strong, and if you are thoughtful about how you represent your work in the classroom, your evaluators will be supportive of your desire to create a more challenging and engaging classroom experience.[24]

Conclusion

Change is hard. Fortunately, we have the benefit of an enormous amount of pedagogical research and years of case method pedagogy in other fields to back these curricular changes. Take courage. When planning your course, keep in mind that preparation is key and remember the following:

- Build the semester around the discipline-specific skills and habits of mind that you wish to foster in your students.
- Resist the urge to fall back into the habit of lecturing or delivering content verbally in the classroom.
- Include only elements in the course that support your learning outcomes and have been proven pedagogically effective—no matter the pressure from colleagues or students.

Notes

1 Radiohead, "Everything in its Right Place," track one on *Kid A,* Parlophone, 2000.
2 Stephen Rumph, *Mozart and Enlightenment Semiotics* (Berkeley: University of California Press, 2011), *ProQuest Ebook Central*, https://ebookcentral. proquest.com/lib/ithaca-ebooks/detail.action?docID=847474

3 Rumph, *Mozart and Enlightenment Semiotics.*

4 The readings, respectively, were Marcia Citron, "Gender, Professionalism, and the Canon," *The Journal of Musicology* 8, no. 1 (1990): 102–117; George Lewis, "Improvised Music after 1950: Afrological and Eurological Perspectives," *Black Music Research Journal* 16, no. 1 (Spring, 1996): 91–122; and Milton Babbitt, "Who Cares if You Listen?" *High Fidelity* (February 1958): 38–40+.

5 Take, for example, this quotation from Immanuel Kant:

> Women, in general, don't like any art, are not well versed in any, and have no talent for it. They can acquire knowledge ... and all that can be acquired through hard work. But that celestial fire that emblazens and ignites the soul, that quality of genius that consumes and devours, ... those sublime ecstasies that reside in the depths of the heart—these will always be lacking in the writings of women.

> *Lettre à M. Alembert sur spectacles* [Amsterdam, 1758], 139n, quoted in Citron, "Gender, Professionalism, and the Canon," 111.

6 Since this class in 2018, the article has been substantially updated, and this imbalance has been corrected. However, gender imbalance on Wikipedia continues to be a problem. See Shlomit Aharoni Lir, "Strangers in a Seemingly Open-to-All Website: The Gender Bias in Wikipedia," *Equality, Diversity and Inclusion: An International Journal* 40, no. 7 (October 2021): 801–818.

7 See Grant P. Wiggins and Jay McTighe, *Understanding by Design*, 2nd ed. (Alexandria, VA: Association for Supervision and Curriculum Development, 2005).

8 James, "How Not to Listen to *Lemonade*," 69–76.

9 Tamara Levitz, "Racism at the Rite," in *The Rite of Spring at 100,* Severine Neff et al. eds., 146–180 (Bloomington, IN: Indiana University Press, 2017).

10 Jonathan Petropoulos, "Art as Propaganda: The Nazi Degenerate Art Exhibit," *Facing History and Ourselves* (accessed July 7, 2020), www.facinghistory.org/resource-library/video/art-propaganda-nazi-degenerate-art-exhibit

11 "The Nazis' take on 'Degenerate Music'" *Deutsche Welle* (accessed July 7, 2020), www.dw.com/en/the-nazis-take-on-degenerate-music/a-16834697

12 Julia L. Foulkes, "Streets and Stages: Urban Renewal and the Arts After World War II," *Journal of Social History* 44, no. 2, (Winter 2010): 413–434, www.jstor.org/stable/25790364

13 John Cage, "Experimental Music," in *Silence: Lectures and Writings,* 7–12 (Middletown, CT: Wesleyan University Press, 1973).

14 Paul Steinbeck, "Introduction," in *Message to Our Folks,* 1–8 (Chicago: University of Chicago Press, 2017).

15 Mattijs van de Port, "Genuinely Made Up: Camp, Baroque, and Other Denaturalizing Aesthetics and the Cultural Production of the Real,"

The Journal of the Royal Anthropological Institute 18, no. 4 (December 2012): 864–883, www.jstor.org/stable/23321454

16 The notion of a "usable past" challenges the notion that "history"—as a discipline—or "culture"—as an object of study—belongs exclusively to the intellectual and social elite. See William J. Bouwsma, *A Usable Past: Essays in European Cultural History* (Berkeley: University of California Press, 1990), 1–9.

17 John Spilker, "Foregrounding Diversity and Inclusion through Innovative Music History Course Design," College Music Society Annual Conference, San Antonio, October 26, 2017, www.music.org/pdf/conf/natl/2017/abstra cts.pdf; John Spilker, "Adventures in 'Survey Adjacent' Music History Courses," *Musicology Now,* November 16, 2017, www.musicologynow.org/2017/11/adventures-in-survey-adjacent-music.html. The descriptions of the courses given on the Nebraska Wesleyan website give no indication of this chronological division.

18 John Spilker, "Syllabus: Music History I: Gender & Sexualities," unpublished document.

19 Personal communication, February 28, 2022, and Trudi Wright, "Cura Personalis: Caring for Ourselves?," Teaching Music History Conference, Boston, June 9, 2017.

20 William Robin, "What Controversial Changes at Harvard Mean for Music in the University," *National Sawdust,* April 25, 2017, https://nationalsawd ust.org/thelog/2017/04/25/what-controversial-changes-at-harvard-means-for-music-in-the-university/

21 There are a number of web-based resources that connect Bloom's Taxonomy with action verbs. I adapted this table from Jessica Shabatura, "Using Bloom's Taxonomy to Write Effective Learning Objectives" Assignments & Measuring Student Learning, University of Arkansas Teaching Innovation and Pedagogical Support (TIPS), September 27, 2013, https://tips.uark.edu/using-blooms-taxonomy/

22 Robin James, "How Not to Listen to *Lemonade:* Music Criticism and Epistemic Violence," in *The Lemonade Reader: Beyoncé, Black Feminism and Spirituality,* Kinitra D. Brooks and Kameelah L. Martin, eds., 75 (New York: Routledge, 2019).

23 Epsen Andersen and Bill Schiano, *Teaching with Cases: A Practical Guide* (Boston: Harvard Business School Publishing, 2014), 12.

24 See Peter Seldin, Elizabeth Miller, and Clement A. Seldin, *The Teaching Portfolio: A Practical Guide to Improved Performance and Promotion/Tenure Decisions,* 4th ed. (San Francisco: Jossey-Bass, 2010).

3 Selecting, Writing, and Reading Cases

I opened Chapter 2 with a sample case study on musical topics that used Chapter One "From Rhetoric to Semiotics" of Stephen Rumph's book *Mozart and Enlightenment Semiotics* to prepare students for class discussion and further inquiry. The chapter was a difficult one, and yet students were able to connect the sophisticated material to their own experiences as performers and listeners. It is a challenge to find reading assignments that hit the "sweet spot" for students; materials written for a popular audience are often too simplistic, and scholarly articles sometimes require a level of sophistication beyond the typical undergraduate student's capabilities.

There is value to assigning challenging readings, but I don't recommend doing it very often. I try to vary the difficulty of the reading and listening assignments, as well as the media type, to engage learners who might be weak readers but who can process auditory information well. I try to draw on a wide range of materials from primary sources and scores, to scholarly articles and book chapters, to materials created for a general audience. The growing work in public musicology is an excellent resource for instructors teaching case studies. Open access materials, blogs, and podcasts written and produced by scholars and practitioners are very often rich in content and yet written for a non-specialist audience. (See Appendix 2 for more information.) This chapter offers, first, examples of materials that can be used as the focus of a case study and, second, tips on writing your own cases. The chapter closes with strategies to teach students how to engage with scholarly writing and listening/score reading assignments. I offer here sample assignments that help students prepare for an in-class discussion of the case study.

DOI: 10.4324/9781003130482-3

Potential Sources for Case Study Materials

Open Access and Common Subscription Materials

"Open access" refers to a relatively new form of academic publishing that is generally high-quality, peer-reviewed, and freely available online. For example, *Open Access Musicology* (*OAM*) publishes peer- and student-reviewed, scholarly essays that are "methodologically transparent models for student research."[1] The essays, on diverse topics, introduce students to a variety of musicological subjects of study and modes of inquiry. Each author begins with an autobiographical introduction that describes how the author became interested in their area of research. Students learn from these introductions how research can be relevant to the researcher's musicianship and personally exciting. The articles are rich with examples of musical notations and include embedded video and audio examples and hyperlinked sources.

For example, Sarah Williams's *OAM* article "An Intermedia Approach to Seventeenth-Century English Popular Song Culture" discusses how popular songs appear in multiple settings, such as published instrumental collections and other entertainment media, including plays. She claims that an intermedia study of popular song requires an understanding of interconnected (and often competing) commercial interests, as well as an exploration of the musical tastes and practices of different socioeconomic groups. While Williams's study focuses on a specific time and place, the article clearly demonstrates that a similar methodological approach can be applied elsewhere. Such a study, she argues, "can reveal a society's priorities, politics, gender and class dynamics, economic trends, tastes, and cultural anxieties."[2]

Naxos Musicology International is similar to *OAM* in that the writing is accessible and the subject matter is diverse, but it is only accessible through a subscription service. *Naxos Musicology International* is part of the Naxos Music Library and intentionally links the content of the articles to recordings found in the *Naxos* collection. The essay "Faces of Tango," by Kacey Link and Kristin Wendland, for example, addresses the history of tango and its style elements (rhythm, melody, harmony, form, instrumentation, and the extended techniques called *yeites*). The essay then discusses specific tango recordings in the Naxos collection.[3]

Many Open Access materials, including textbooks such as Danielle Fosler-Lussier's *Music on the Move* and Esther Morgan-Ellis's *Resonances: Engaging Music in Its Cultural Context*, are published with a Creative Commons 4.0 International License.[4] This copyright license "allows you to remix, tweak, and build upon this work, even commercially, as long as you credit this original source for the creation and license the new creation under identical terms."[5] This flexibility is ideal for crafting case study readings that can appropriately challenge students. It also allows students to be participants in the creation of knowledge through their own additions, extensions, or remixes of open access materials.

Blogs

While anyone with internet access can author a blog, there are a number of them hosted by reputable publishers, record labels, or media outlets. W. W. Norton & Company hosts *The Avid Listener*, which was designed to supplement and diversify the content of the *History of Western Music* textbook and its accompanying anthology. *The Avid Listener* publishes music commentary and criticism pitched to an undergraduate reader. Each post includes numerous hyperlinks, embedded video or musical examples, as well as three to four discussion questions designed for student engagement.

I often assign my own contributions to this blog because in them I address fundamental ideological problems endemic to the study of music history: for example, the constructedness of the historical record, the genius construct, teleological historical narratives, and the Cartesian dualism that has excluded the body from the study of music.[6] Other authors' posts address similar issues as well as individual works or musical moments. For example, Ann van Allen-Russell's post "Stop Copying My Music!: The Emergence of Musical Copyright in England" uses J. C. Bach's lawsuits against English publishers as a way to introduce issues involving copyright standards in the eighteenth century.[7] Students are often curious about copyright issues but that subject is missing from or is underdeveloped in most textbooks.

Another blog, *New Music Box*, publishes contributions from scholars, composers, performers, and critics with a focus on new compositions and ensembles specializing in new music performance. This blog is published by New Music USA, an organization that grew out of Meet the Composer and the American Music Center. The articles here often address music in our current sociopolitical context. For example, Karl Ronnenburg's article "On Performing Fluxus in 2020" addresses issues related to musical performance during a pandemic and suggests that Fluxus-inspired works are a good solution to the problem that social distancing has introduced to musical performance. The article includes a brief history of Fluxus, with several examples of Fluxus events.[8]

Podcasts

Podcasts are ideal because they can seamlessly combine scholarship with musical examples. They also give students who are good auditory learners a break from trying to decode academic writing. For example, The Society for Ethnomusicology's *Ethnomusicology Today* podcast broadly addresses "contemporary issues in global music studies."[9] Each episode features an author of a recent article published in the journal *Ethnomusicology*. The interviews combine a clear summary of the content with insights into research methods and sounds from the field. For example, Episode 9, "Performative Ecology in Micronesia with Brian Diettrich," focuses on the question, How does music interact with ecological concerns? Diettrich's study, published in the Winter 2018 issue, looks at both historical and current musical practices in Micronesia. His focus is on "breadfruit summoning" songs and dances. Diettrich explains how such performances are closely tied to social, economic, spiritual, and environmental concerns.[10]

The podcast *American Songster* explores American roots music. Episode 3 of season 2 unsettles the stereotypical image of the white singing cowboy with a brief introduction to black songwriters included in anthologies of cowboy songs, starting with John Lomax's *Cowboy Songs* collection from 1911. The discussion leads to Lomax's "discovery" of Lead Belly and his song "When I Was a Cowboy," making an overt connection between "the blues, folk music, and cowboy poetry."[11]

Will Robins's *Sound Expertise* features interviews with musicologists with diverse research interests, perspectives, and identities about their recent work. Each podcast is accompanied by a list of recommended readings and recordings for further listening. Like *OAM*, these podcasts not only explore the product of each scholar's work but also often lay bare the process of research. Robin's conversation with Micaela K. Baranello, for example, explores what Viennese operetta can tell us about everyday life in fin-de-siècle Vienna, in contrast to what we learn about the city through high-art composers such as Mahler and Schoenberg.[12]

Episode 3 of Andrew Granade and David Thurmaier's podcast, *Hearing the Pulitzers*, explores Aaron Copland's *Appalachian Spring* and could be used to amplify a study of the piece within a traditional music history survey.[13] Episode 9, in contrast, features the 1951 winner, Douglas Moore, and his opera *Giants in the Earth*, for which there are no commercial recordings and no performances since 1974.[14] This episode could inspire discussions of the purpose of prizes such as The Pulitzer.

Hosted by Rhiannon Giddens, each episode of *Aria Code* explores a single opera aria with guests from the operatic world. The episode "Puccini's Turandot: Bewitched, Bothered, And Beheaded," for example, places Princess Turandot's first aria, "In questa reggia," in the context of the entire opera.[15] Sopranos Christine Goerke, Renée Fleming, and author Will Berger discuss the text, the emotional world of the aria, and its technical demands.

The podcast *Song Exploder* features discussions of a song's compositional history, production, and meaning with the artists that created it. Individual musical elements are often isolated and highlighted in musical examples and often placed within a larger analysis of the song's form. Each podcast ends with the song in its entirety. Billie Eilish's "Everything I Wanted," coproduced with her brother, Finneas O'Connell, is the subject of Episode 197.[16] The episode starts with a description of a dream that Eilish had of her own suicide that inspired the composition of the song. Eilish and O'Connell discuss how specific musical figures and production effects shape the mood of the song and amplify the text.

Dedicated to music from Africa and the African diaspora, the podcast *Afropop Worldwide* looks at musical styles, performers, and scenes and their musical, cultural, and political significance. Episode 824 on Reggaetón and Race, for example, describes the style's underground roots and its depiction of life in the inner-city housing projects of Puerto Rico.[17] Guest Petra Rivera-Rideau, author of the book *Remixing Reggaetón: The Cultural Politics of Race in Puerto Rico*, describes the persistent "racist and sexist undertones of the genre's constant policing" in Puerto Rico as well as in the Dominican Republic and Cuba.

Each episode of *Meet the Composer* is hosted by violist Nadia Sirota and offers an in-depth exploration of the work of a contemporary classical composer and is accompanied by a "bonus track" that focuses on a single piece and a complete performance of the work. The composer typically describes the piece, and a performer discusses the challenges or joys of performing it. The May 1, 2017, episode features Henry Threadgill.[18] Threadgill describes his background growing up in Chicago, his military service in Vietnam, and his time with the Association for the Advancement of Creative Musicians (AACM). He talks about his compositional and rehearsal processes and the limits of notation. The bonus track features Threadgill's ensemble Zooid performing live at the Village Vanguard in 2016.[19]

The August 17, 2020, episode of *Classically Speaking* describes the commission and composition process of three works by Jennifer Higdon: her 2017 *Low Brass Concerto*, the middle school band piece *Rhythm Stand*, and perhaps her best-known work, *blue cathedral.*[20] Higdon also describes her musical influences, including rock, country, and the Beatles.

Dissect features "long-form musical analysis," often combining the vocabulary of music theory with historical contextualization. The podcast devotes each season to a single hip hop or R&B album, with an episode devoted to each song on the album. An excellent example is the discussion of the song "Doo Wop (That Thing)," from Lauryn Hill's album *The Miseducation of Lauryn Hill,* in episode 4 of miniseries 1.[21] The episode untangles threads of doo wop and hip hop woven together in Hill's song, with a discussion of the origins and attributes of both styles. An analysis of the lyrics reveals Hill's critique of hip-hop culture and its often superficial approach to materialism, religious belief, and sexuality.

Podcasts are a great tool for bringing music-historical scenes to life through sound—with musical examples as well as the voices of those who are creating, researching, or promoting the music.

Long-form Journalism

Newspapers and magazines such as *The New York Times* and *The New Yorker* publish long-form journalism written by music critics. But they also feature the work of academics. Such articles benefit from the fast pen-to-publication timeline, and scholars are able to connect their academic work to current events in an engaging and accessible writing style. These are more substantial than typical reviews or news articles, and they might have a more narrative or personal point of view. Recent examples include articles by Kyra Gaunt, Kerry O'Brien, and Doug Shadle.

In her *New York Times* article "The Magic of Black Girls' Play," Gaunt writes about the power of rhymed and metered musical games and how they "are a way for Black girls to learn how social relationships are negotiated within America's racialized and sexist map of reality." Gaunt unpacks the African diasporic aesthetics and coded language embedded in playground chants and argues that they teach collaboration and engender a sense of worthiness in Black girls.[22]

O'Brien has championed the work of experimental composers Annea Lockwood, Ellen Fullman, and Pauline Oliveros in the popular press.[23] Her 2016 *New Yorker* article describes how Oliveros's collection of conceptual pieces, *Sonic Meditations*, is rooted in therapeutic practices such as Tai Chi and Kinetic Awareness. Oliveros studied these and other bodywork practices in response to the turmoil of the 1960s. O'Brien argues that the *Sonic Meditations* emerge from an intersection of group meditation, improvisation, women's liberation, and political embodiment.

Shadle's *New York Times* article "Did Dvořák's 'New World' Symphony Transform American Music?" challenges the long-held historical narrative that the symphony demonstrated for the first time how classical music might sound "American." Shadle narrates how the composers Louis Moreau Gottshalk and Henry Schoenefeld were borrowing "Creole" and "Negro" melodies in order to create an American musical idiom already in the mid-nineteenth century. He also provides evidence that this music was well known in Europe before Dvořák set sail for the United States.[24]

Popular scholarship, exemplified by the work mentioned above, can amplify and challenge the existing music historical narrative and inspire questions about who is and should be included in the history, what kinds of musical practices are valued as objects of study, and what constitutes "prestige" in the historical narrative.

Writing Cases

The advantage of using published scholarly articles and public scholarship as preparatory assignments is that they include more than just facts about music history; indeed, most scholarship includes an analysis and interpretation of data, and scholars often make a claim for the significance of their work. Such work is an excellent model for students to emulate. The disadvantage to assigning such work to students, however, is that they do not give students ample opportunity to develop the musicological skills of analysis and interpretation on their own. You may decide instead to write your own cases that present data about a case, but withhold an interpretation or analysis of the data. The analysis and interpretation, then, will happen in classroom discussion and in subsequent small group work.

Adapting published scholarship for a case study requires removing the author's interpretation and analysis in order to foreground the facts. This approach is analogous to a physician presenting a patient's medical history and current symptoms to a group of students who are then asked to make a diagnosis and decide on a treatment plan. The medical instructor will want to give just enough information so that the students can begin to ask their own questions to analyze the case.

An excellent candidate for such an adaptation is Javier Marín-López's 2008 article "The Musical Inventory of Mexico Cathedral, 1589: A Lost Document."[25] López uses a sixteenth-century document to reconstruct the polyphonic repertory performed in the Mexico Cathedral. The inventory includes printed collections of works by European composers (such as Josquin, Morales, Verdelot, Lassus, and Victoria) alongside local composers (such as the brothers Francisco and Pedro Guerrero). It also includes music from a variety of genres—liturgical and extra-liturgical—including the vernacular *villancico* and *chanzoneta*.

An adaptation of an article for a case study should do two things: first, it should tell a compelling story, and second, it should clearly present the facts of the case. If the adaptation were simply a list of the contents of the newly discovered inventory of the Mexican Cathedral, the students would not be impelled to read it. But this document was created at a tumultuous time, shortly after the fall of Tenochtitlan, in 1521, and the Spanish conquest of the Aztec Empire. Moreover, the Mexico Cathedral was built on the site of the Aztec Temple. The case needs to tell some of this story to motivate the students to want to learn the facts of the case. See Appendix 3 for more discussion of how I adapted the article as a case study and my adaptation.

Figure 3.1 depicts the research process for students. A case narrative will cover the first stages of the process; it will illuminate the context of the topic, the research question, and the methodology for data collection. The case narrative will conclude after a clear presentation of the research—what I called the "facts" of the case. Withholding your own expert analysis and interpretation of the data gives students an opportunity to learn how to be, as Andersen and Schiano put it, "qualitative about the quantitative."[26] In other words, it gives students an opportunity to discuss the historical evidence, to discover what it might mean, and to make their own assertions about what value it might have. This approach also gives students the opportunity to pose new research questions given the evidence at hand. The evidence in the case study on the musical inventory of the Mexico Cathedral details "the musico-liturgical needs of a single institution at a given moment,"[27] but it can also inspire larger questions about the prominence of European music and instruments used in the New World shortly after colonization.

Reading Cases

Reading a music-historical primary or secondary source means to join a conversation that is often hundreds of years old. And because most students don't yet know how to join that conversation, likely because

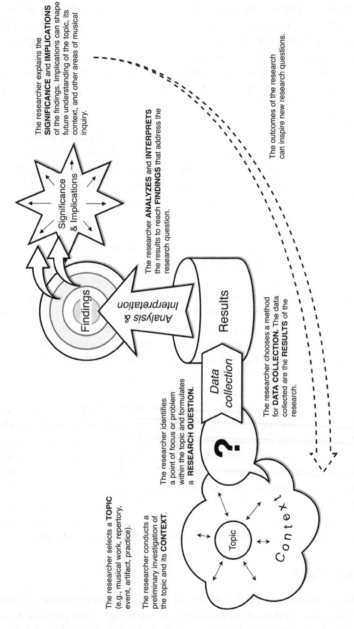

Figure 3.1 The Research Process, *Writing in Music: A Brief Guide.*

they don't understand its rules or conventions, I introduce them to research that makes explicit musicological habits of mind. Figure 3.1 can help prompt students to identify not only the topic of the study but also the research question, the method of data collection, and the author's findings. It also cues the student to look for how the author is analyzing and interpreting the results of their research and perhaps to understand that the same data might be interpreted differently. Finally, as the student takes note of the author's claims, they might be inspired to ask further research questions of their own.

Reading the abstract of a secondary source can give students a road map, as all of the items in the diagram should be stated explicitly in the abstract. I also suggest reverse outlining an article or book chapter with an eye for keywords and strategic rhetorical moves, such as "I argue that..." or "I conclude that..." Students can do this pre-class study collaboratively and, in fact, doing so introduces them to more reading and interpretive strategies as they observe how their peers navigate scholarly writings.

If the pre-case assignment involves listening to and/or studying a score, then I suggest giving the students guidance on what to listen and look for:

- Make note of your first impressions. What grabs your attention? What causes a physical or emotional reaction?
- What is the style and genre?
- Where, when, and who created and/or performed it?
- What is the form? (Think both large and small scale.)
- How are sounds organized according to pitch and time?
- What is the instrumentation? Which timbres are significant?
- If the piece has a text, what does it mean? How does it interact with the music?[28]

This close guidance is ideally unnecessary later in the course when students have internalized the skills mentioned in these instructions.

To help students prepare to discuss the artifact, I have them respond to questions before class on the course learning management system. The questions take the students from a basic understanding to interpretation and evaluation of the source. For example, for James's book chapter, "How Not to Listen to *Lemonade*," I ask:

1 Who is the author and what are their credentials?
2 What is the central question of this book chapter?
3 What does the author mean by "epistemic violence"?

4   Who are the following people?
   a   Ma Rainey
   b   Bessie Smith
   c   Dolly Parton
   d   Donna Summer
   e   Aretha Franklin

There were also several difficult sentences in the reading that I wanted students to come to terms with:

5   What does the following sentence (bottom of page 73) mean?
    "As Jennifer Stoever-Ackerman has argued, even though Western modernity's occularcentric epistemology obscures the sonic dimensions of white supremacist patriarchy and the subaltern knowledge developed under it, sounds nevertheless work politically."
    Can you rephrase it in a simpler way?

I also wanted students to begin to interpret the article, and prompted them to do so with questions that are not answered in the article, such as the following:

6   Does the reception of Beyoncé have anything to do with the "mind/body problem," otherwise known as "Cartesian dualism"? Explain.

I have found that having students answer these questions before class discussion (1) ensures that students understand the content of the reading and (2) encourages them to begin to analyze or evaluate its contents. I encourage students to work collaboratively before class to prepare for discussion. Students can ask for clarification from each other or sound out ideas informally in small groups. After submitting their answers, either on the discussion forum or as an assignment, students are ready for discussion of the case in class. These pre-case questions give the students sufficient introduction to the case, but these questions are not asked or necessarily answered in class. In fact, in order to prevent potential frustrations, students should understand that this work is *preparatory* to the classroom discussion but will not necessarily be the content of the discussion. In other words, class will not include a recital of these answers.

When working with more advanced students and/or more accessible artifacts, I ask students to post before class a few paragraphs about the case on an online discussion board. I offer students a template for these "mini essays"; this one was created by the writing pedagogue Cory Brown:

I haven't thought much about the self, philosophically, apart from having *experienced* a self, presumably having one myself, but as I think about it now I realize that I have been carrying around some preconceptions about it all my life, mostly without knowing it, and this is what they are: [an explanation of preconceptions]. With those preconceptions in mind, I've just read a chapter in V.S. Ramachandran's book *The Tell Tale Brain*, and this is what he explains about what the self is: [summary of the argument].

Now that I've read his analysis, I can analyze my preconceptions in that context, and I believe I've changed my thinking to incorporate some of his insights. I think he's right that the self is not as stable as we typically think, given how many different parts of the brain contribute to all the characteristics of the self he describes and that we think define a self.

But I have a couple of bones to pick with Ramachandran, particularly about two of those characteristics he lists: [a rebuttal of the argument].

Now I have to admit, after wrestling with Ramachandran's conceptions of two of the traditional characteristics of self, that there may be a characteristic of the self that isn't on his list, one that calls for a different view of the self than I, and possibly even Ramachandran himself, had considered: [new insight or extension of the argument].

Finally, this is what I've concluded about this fascinating topic, to the best of my knowledge: [concluding thoughts].[29]

The benefit of the more unstructured response is that I can check for comprehension before class, and noting apparent gaps in understanding helps me prepare for the class discussion. The examples that students use in these mini-essays can also serve as in-class examples for further discussion, and the student author will be ready to take the lead.

Below is a strong student example from the case study on musical topics. For this case study, the students read Chapter One "From Rhetoric to Semiotics" of Stephen Rumph's book *Mozart and Enlightenment Semiotics*.[30] I provided the following instructions:

> **Instructions:** Feel free to discuss any aspect of the reading and listening assignment. Think in particular about the following:
>
> 1. The title of this section of the book is called "From Rhetoric to Semiotics." Look up a definition of both of those terms and

define them in your own words. Why is a distinction important? How can either term be applied to music?

2. On page 21 the author claims that "Operatic rhetoric relied upon a lexicon of conventional signs through which characters could communicate their emotions and desires." What does this mean? Can you give examples of "conventional signs" in music, either from the classical repertoire or from later styles, including today?

3. Post questions you probably have about this difficult content.

Here is the student's discussion forum post:

Prior to reading this article, I had very little background knowledge of opera, so I had never heard of any of the operatic rhetorical devices mentioned by this book's author before. Based on Merriam Webster's definitions, I would define rhetoric as the skill of speaking effectively, and semiotics as the study of symbols and signs in languages. Using these definitions, it seems that rhetoric in music is how a composer or performer conveys a message to their audience (or, as the book mentions, to other characters on stage), whether that message is a mood or an extramusical idea, and whether or not that music also uses words. Semiotics could refer to musical gestures that an audience has emotional associations with; these change based on the audience's location and time period, with some obvious ones for the present in Western music being minor keys and slow tempos acting as a symbol to convey sadness, and dissonance and resolution commonly conveying distress and peace. In other words, it seems that in music, the symbols described by semiotics are a useful rhetorical tool.

When the author says, "Operatic rhetoric relied upon a lexicon of conventional signs through which characters could communicate their emotions and desires," I believe they are referring to these musical gestures commonly used to convey certain moods or messages. The roles of these gestures were solidified by years of opera repertoire until they became commonly understood by opera audiences; this is why a more inexperienced listener like myself might miss some of them. Some, such as the Mannheim sigh, rely upon existing aspects of human speech—sighs can communicate exasperation or longing, and apparently the Mannheim sigh serves a similar purpose for opera characters. In the case of Cherubino's aria, these sighs are only suggested by Mozart's use of appoggiaturas until the last line, when the tempo slows and the lyrics become more reflective. I think a lot of Mozart's operatic rhetoric here could also be described as text painting—using musical signs to portray the text of the opera's libretto.

Another student connected the content of the chapter to their current composition project and text painting. This student included in their post a link to Kate Soper's "Only the Words Themselves Mean What They Say," a piece that this student admires, particularly for its effective and evocative text setting.

A good case narrative—whether it be one designed for students or for interested lifelong learners—will be inspired by a good research problem and should inspire further inquiry. A good narrative will also allow the students to develop their own analytical and interpretive skills. Finding such narratives (or writing them yourself) is only half the battle; teaching students how to read and engage with scholarly writing and thinking is the other half. In any case, students should come to class having read a case study narrative ready and eager for discussion.

Notes

1 "Submissions," *Open Access Musicology,* accessed February 15, 2022, https://openaccessmusicology.wordpress.com/submissions/
2 Sarah F. Williams, "An Intermedia Approach to Seventeenth-Century English Popular Song Culture," in *Open Access Musicology* 1, Louis Epstein and Daniel Barolsky, eds. (Amherst, MA: Lever Press, 2020), https://doi.org/10.3998/mpub.12063224
3 Kacey Link and Kristin Wendland, "Faces of Tango," *Naxos Musicology International,* August 20, 2020, www.naxosmusicology.com/essays/faces-of-tango/
4 Danielle Fosler-Lussier, *Music on the Move* (Ann Arbor, MI: University of Michigan Press, 2020) and Esther M. Morgan-Ellis, ed., *Resonances Engaging Music in Its Cultural Context* (Blue Ridge, GA: University of North Georgia Press, 2021).
5 Morgan-Ellis, *Resonances*, ii. See also "Attribution-NonCommercial 4.0 International (CC BY-NC 4.0)," *Creative Commons,* accessed March 3, 2022, https://creativecommons.org/licenses/by-nc/4.0/
6 Sara Haefeli, "If History Is Written by the Victors," updated July 23, 2020, https://theavidlistenerblog.com/2020/07/23/if-history20-is-written-by-the-victors/; "The Problem with Geniuses," updated July 24, 2020, https://theavidlistenerblog.com/2020/07/24/the-problem-with-geniuses/; "Does Music Evolve?" updated July 23, 2020, https://theavidlistenerblog.com/2020/07/23/does-music-evolve/; "How Musicology Became That Town in Footloose," updated July 24, 2020, https://theavidlistenerblog.com/2020/07/24/how-musicology-became-that-town-in-footloose/

7 Ann van Allen-Russell, "Stop Copying My Music!: The Emergence of Musical Copyright in England," *The Avid Listener,* updated July 28, 2020, https://theavidlistenerblog.com/2020/07/28/stop-copying-my-music-the-emergence-of-musical-copyright-in-england/

8 Karl Ronnenburg, "On Performing Fluxus in 2020," *New Music Box,* October 27, 2020, https://nmbx.newmusicusa.org/on-performing-fluxus-in-2020/

9 "Ethnomusicology Today," *The Society for Ethnomusicology* (website), accessed February 15, 2022, www.ethnomusicology.org/members/group_content_view.asp?group=156353&id=534562

10 "Performative Ecology in Micronesia with Brian Diettrich," *Ethnomusicology Today,* February 8, 2019, www.ethnomusicology.org/members/group_conte nt_view.asp?group=156353&id=784808

11 Don Flemons, "Lead Belly, 'The Singing Cowboy," *American Songster Radio,* October 26, 2018, www.wunc.org/post/lead-belly-singing-cowboy-american-songster-radio-season-2-episode-3

12 Micaela Baranello and Will Robin, "Operetta and Fin-de-siècle Vienna," *Sound Expertise,* episode 105, https://soundexpertise.org/operetta-and-fin-de-siecle-vienna-with-micaela-baranello/

13 Andrew Granade and David Thurmaier, "Aaron Copland, Appalachian Spring," *Hearing the Pulitzers,* March 8, 2020, https://hearingthepulitzers. podbean.com/e/episode-3-1944-aaron-copland-appalachian-spring/

14 Andrew Granade and David Thurmaier, "Douglas Moore, Giants in the Earth," *Hearing the Pulitzers,* August 15, 2020, https://hearingthepulitzers. podbean.com/e/episode-9-1951-douglas-moore-giants-in-the-earth/

15 Rhiannon Giddens and Merrin Lazyan, "Puccini's Turandot: Bewitched, Bothered, and Beheaded," *Aria Code,* January 22, 2020, www.wnycstudios. org/podcasts/aria-code/episodes/aria-code-puccini-turandot-christine-goerke

16 Hrishikesh Hirway, "Billie Eilish: 'Everything I Wanted,'" *Song Exploder,* November 18, 2020, https://songexploder.net/billie-eilish

17 Luis López, "Reggaetón and Race," *Afropop Worldwide,* August 5, 2021, https://afropop.org/audio-programs/reggaet%C3%B3n-and-race

18 "Henry Threadgill: Dirt, and More Dirt," *Meet the Composer,* May 1, 2017, www.newsounds.org/story/henry-threadgill-dirt-and-more-dirt

19 "Henry Threadgill's Zooid, Live at the Village Vanguard," *Meet the Composer,* May 8, 2017, www.newsounds.org/story/henry-threadgills-zooid-live-village-vanguard

20 Colleen Phelps, "Classically Speaking: Bespoke Music Making with Jennifer Higdon," *Nashville Classical Radio,* August 17, 2020, https://91classical.org/post/classically-speaking-bespoke-music-making-with-jennifer-higdon/

21 "'Doo Wop (That Thing)' by Lauryn Hill," *Dissect,* November 27, 2018, https://anchor.fm/dissect/episodes/MS1E4---Doo-Wop-That-Thing-by-Lauryn-Hill-e2ho3d

22 Kyra Gaunt, "The Magic of Black Girls' Play," *The New York Times,* July 21, 2020, updated July 23, 2020, www.nytimes.com/2020/07/21/parenting/black-girls-play.html?fbclid=IwAR02hrWCvaHraeaDOpQxlGUoomDf2 Y5A_hH4-EALuTXSjPZwXYV553UcYVc

23 Kerry O'Brien, "Burning Pianos and Whispering Rivers: A Composer's Journey," *The New York Times,* Nov. 8, 2019, www.nytimes.com/2019/11/08/arts/music/annea-lockwood-miller-theater.html?searchResultPosition= 1; "A Composer and Her (Very) Long String Instrument," *The New York Times,* May 1, 2020, www.nytimes.com/2020/05/01/arts/music/ellen-fullman.html?searchResultPosition=2; and "Listening as Activism: The "Sonic Meditations" of Pauline Oliveros," December 9, 2016, www.newyorker.com/culture/culture-desk/listening-as-activism-the-sonic-meditations-of-pauline-oliveros

24 Doug Shadle, "Did Dvorak's 'New World' Symphony Transform American Music?" *The New York Times,* December 14, 2018, www.nytimes.com/2018/12/14/arts/music/dvorak-new-world-symphony.html

25 Thank you to Kimary Fick for introducing me to this article in the context of case study analysis. Javier Marín-López, "The Musical Inventory of Mexico Cathedral, 1589: A Lost Document," *Early Music* 36, no. 4 (November 2008): 575–596, doi:10.1093/em/can094. Fick's discussion of this material can be found in "Systems of Power, Privilege, and Oppression: Towards A Social Justice Education Pedagogy for Music History Curricula," *Journal of Music History Pedagogy* 12, no. 1 (2022): 46–67.

26 Epsen Andersen and Bill Schiano, *Teaching with Cases: A Practical Guide* (Boston: Harvard Business School Publishing, 2014), 175.

27 López, "The Musical Inventory of Mexico Cathedral," abstract.

28 Lynne Rogers, Karen Bottge, and Sara Haefeli, *Writing in Music: A Brief Guide* (Oxford: Oxford University Press, 2020), 5.

29 Cory Brown, unpublished document, 2020.

30 Stephen Rumph, *Mozart and Enlightenment Semiotics* (Berkeley, CA: University of California Press, 2011), *ProQuest Ebook Central,* https://ebookcentral.proquest.com/lib/ithaca-ebooks/detail.action?docID=847474

4   Class Discussion

Andersen and Schiano describe the ideal case study teacher as one "who does not say much, but instead gently guides the discussion like a comfortable, benevolent, and slightly distant Socrates." They describe a process that should, in theory, be quite simple: "you ask a student to open the discussion and gently but firmly steer the students' discussion through the case and the topics by posing questions and signaling who should speak next, while capturing notes on the boards."[1] In reality, the idea of guiding the discussion of a case is often anxiety provoking for the instructor, especially for those accustomed to lecturing. On the one hand, we worry about students' preparation for a rich discussion, and on the other, we are concerned about our own ability to extemporaneously ask probing questions that will guide the discussion productively. Choosing to discuss a case rather than lecture means giving up control: control of the content that is covered in class as well as over the unfolding of the class period, to some extent. However, despite the anxiety that it may initially provoke for the instructor, giving up control brings great gifts: students are much more likely to happen upon questions, problems, and ideas during the discussion that are new and unexpected, or they might bring up unforeseen and interesting examples. But most importantly, students will have the opportunity to take control—empowering them to shape and take responsibility for their own learning experience.

This chapter discusses ways to support a shift of control from professor to student that can tip the scales toward meaningful discussion. There are indeed things you can do to help students engage in productive discussion, starting with setting expectations at the beginning of the semester and setting up your physical classroom for discussion. It also helps to teach students academic literacy and close-listening skills early in the semester so that they can feel prepared to engage with cases that often include difficult reading and listening assignments.

DOI: 10.4324/9781003130482-4

Expectations and Preparation

Students in schools like Harvard Business School understand that discussion is an essential part of the learning process and have classrooms specially designed for case study teaching. These rooms have a stadium, horseshoe layout so that all students can easily see each other and an enormous whiteboard at the front of the room. The vast majority of music schools will not have such a classroom, and students may not be accustomed to a discussion-based classroom. You will have to make your discussion expectations clear at the beginning of the semester and you may have to be creative with your classroom layout.

I include a statement in the syllabus that helps set student expectations about participation:

> Learning in this class will be communal. Productive participation can take multiple forms, including:
>
> - *Yes, And.* Can you find ways to extend the contribution of another? (Add more examples, sources, or experiences.)
> - *Connections with your experiences or prior knowledge.* Can you share how this relates to the experience or knowledge that you came into the class with? (Highlight the ways in which your thinking and/or understanding has changed.)
> - *Clarifying questions.* If something is uncertain or unclear, can you ask for greater clarity?
> - *Imaginative or creative questions.* Ask others some of the question types above (e.g., imagine you were in this situation, what would you do?; or if X event did not happen, what do you think might have been the result?).
> - *Future directions.* Where might one go next?

I also include a syllabus statement about difficult conversations:

> Difficult, controversial topics are part of our musical history and the topics that we're covering in this class are often difficult, not just intellectually but emotionally. While I expect there to be rigorous discussion and even disagreement in the course of our class discussions, I ask that you engage in discussion with care and empathy for the other members in the classroom. Aim to disagree without becoming disagreeable. In this class we will not shy away from the uncomfortable. Critically examining and assessing our most basic assumptions and values is not just one of the tasks of

musical history but is an activity vital to living an authentic life. I urge you to have the courage to confront the uncomfortable in this class. In exchange for your courage, I will work to ensure a classroom environment that supports your taking these intellectual and emotional risks. If you are uncomfortable with upcoming topics or discussions, please come see me so that we can decide together how to address the material in a way that is productive for you.

Introducing classroom norms on the first day is an excellent way to set the tone for future discussions. Alexandra Sedlovskaya, who studies diversity and inclusion in case study teaching, recommends framing classroom discussion norms with four Cs: curiosity, candor, courtesy, and courage.[2]

The physical layout of the classroom also helps to set student expectations about classroom participation and discussion. The point of Harvard Business School's horseshoe, stadium design is to encourage discussion *between* students and to decentralize the classroom power structure. The large whiteboards are used to collect data and vocabulary as the discussion unfolds. If you have a choice, choose a room with moveable desks or tables and orient the room so that students can see each other, preferably in a semicircle, square "U" shape, or anything that promotes more face-to-face discussion.[3]

Case study specialists suggest using name cards and assigned seats. The name cards allow a brisk discussion from the start without the awkwardness of pointing or calling on students based on, say, the color of their shirt. If you are assessing class participation, then assigned seats will be a great help, and I will discuss why this is in Chapter 6. The name cards and assigned seats are especially helpful in large classes, and Andersen and Schiano claim that a case study approach can work even in classes of up to one hundred students.[4]

Doing your own preparatory work before each class is essential. Andersen and Schiano compare prepping cases as an instructor to reading a book like a film director: a normal reader will "focus on the content and understanding the characters." But a film director not only reads for content and understanding, but also thinks about how they can use the material in the film: "Where are the dramatic points I must underscore? [...] How can I make the material come alive through dialogue? How much time should I spend on each part?"[5]

Sample Case Study Discussion

The following section focuses on two cases in order to illustrate discussion preparation and facilitation. The first example explores film music as part of my Music History After 1900 class. The students typically have two to three days to prepare for class and I asked them to do the following:

1 Read (and watch embedded videos): Andrew Farach-Colton, "Three Pioneers of Film Music: Shostakovich, Korngold, and Copland."[6]
2 Read: excerpts from Sally Bick, *Unsettled Scores: Politics, Hollywood, and the Film Music of Aaron Copland & Hans Eisler.*[7]
3 Watch: Opening scene, *Of Mice and Men*, 1939, (score by Copland).
4 Watch: "Battle on the Ice" from *Alexander Nevsky*, 1938, (score by Prokofiev).

Optional videos:

> *The Silly Little Mouse,* 1939, (score by Shostakovich)
> *Winnie the Pooh,* 1969, (score by Mieczysław Weinberg)

Preparing for Discussion

Before class, students wrote a mini-essay on the readings and videos, and an "open" prompt worked perfectly:

> In the discussion forum, feel free to comment on any aspect of the readings or films. You could potentially compare and contrast the film scoring techniques of two or more composers, or analyze a scene as Bick does in the reading assignment. Be sure to reply to at least one other student's post.

Before class, I skimmed the student responses and took brief notes so that I could both call on students whom I knew were prepared and so I could refer to specific content in a student's post and have them explain it to the class or expand upon it. I find that calling on students to extend their discussion forum post gives them confidence, and it can keep the discussion moving when students are silent in response to my questions.

Sample Discussion Forum Notes

AMELIA: great discussion of the difference betw. musicals & movies

RYLEE: factory model of production & politics

LOGAN: politics, esp. Stalin and Russian films

KATE: status & prestige of film composers vs. "art music" composers

ISABELLA: Copland as revolutionary

JULIAN: posted video re. temp music in Marvel movies

OLIVIA: film music describes "inner psychology" not "outer action"

STEPHEN: status; Eisler & Korngold not part of canon

WHITNEY: former TV/film major, has experience matching music to film

[. . .]

Class Plan

Before every class discussion, I make an outline that serves as a rough roadmap for the discussion. "Roadmap" is the perfect metaphor because class discussions often take side trips or detours, or change destinations altogether. *And that's okay.* These outlines usually include three to five points and perhaps a specific quote or two from the reading assignment. I also prepare audio or video examples to support specific points of the discussion, if they come up.[8]

Roadmap for the Film Music Discussion

BASIC DEFINITIONS:

- Diegetic/non-diegetic
- Cues
- Mickey mousing
- Leitmotif
- Gesamtkunstwerk
- Temp music (use Julian's video[9])

STYLE:

- To conform or not to conform?
- Modernism?

STATUS:

* film composers versus "art music" composers

SEMIOTICS:

* Farach-Colton: "Shostakovich had a clear and immediate sense of music's potential to function *not merely as a narrative accessory but as a powerful tool to express psychological, spiritual or even philosophical signs and subtleties.*"
* Farach-Colton: "film music was used to strengthen the emotions of reality, or, to use current terminology, to illustrate the frame. We immediately came to an agreement with [Shostakovich] that the *music would be linked to the inner meaning and not to the external action.*"[10]

Walking into a case study classroom with only an outline and a page of notes on the discussion forum feels far different than walking in with a scripted lecture, an anthology of scores, and a playlist of recordings. Despite the fact that successful case study discussions require thoughtful preparation, you will likely feel unprepared. (And what will your colleagues think if they see you entering class with only a couple of scraps of paper in your hand?) The difference between delivering a lecture and leading a case study discussion is not one of preparation, but one of *control*. It's easy to feel prepared when lecturing because everything is under your own control, but the instructor's sense of control over the classroom comes at the expense of the students who are passive in such an environment. Although I can't control or even predict what the students are going to say during the class, I can guide the discussion using both my notes from the discussion forum and my "roadmap" outline.

Sample Discussion

Despite the lively online discussion before class, getting the discussion off the ground was difficult. After reviewing the recording of the class, I noted that my opening question and several follow-ups simply asked students to define terms or give specific examples. The questions were "closed" questions that could have been answered with just a few words and answers were either right or wrong. But when I asked an open question, the discussion took off:

SH: Many of you wrote in the discussion forum about the status of film composers. Sebastian, I want you to talk about this, if you don't mind.

SEBASTIAN: Yeah, so it just irks me that film composers aren't typically given the credit that a lot of classical composers are when they've been just as innovative in different ways. I'm going to go off on a quick tangent: one thing that film composers do that is so cool to me is they're keeping orchestral music relevant to today's society. And that's a big thing that I don't think they get enough credit for, you know. You get millions and millions to see the new *Star Wars* movie with this booming orchestral score from John Williams. So many people across the world get to see that. Whereas you have much lower turnouts to, say, a concert featuring the works of Beethoven or Mahler or whatnot. So I think that that's something that film composers don't get enough credit for.

SH: Yes, I think you're right. Is it true that film music composers are just as innovative as concert music composers?

WILLOW: I would say yes, because there is this idea that because film composers are often restricted by the structure that they're less creative. However, I feel like this discounts the entire compositional philosophy of, like, restriction breeds creativity. What is serialism but a set of restrictions that you've placed upon yourself? And I think that frequently composers get on their high horse against film composers because they see different skill sets and think, oh, it's not like me. It's not as good. My composition professor said he attended a composition convention where John Williams was, like, *heckled*.

This is a massive problem we have in music of really being Euro-centric. And we've seen it time and time again . . . with vocal music: where we have our "art" music and we have our "theater" music and we have our "jazz" music. But we label only one of those things "art" and everything else is . . . yeah, something else.

SH: Willow mentioned restrictions that film composers have. What are these restrictions? How do directors work with composers to create a score? Julian?

JULIAN: Yeah, I talked about this in my post. There's this huge sort of problematic thing going on with the music industry where directors will put temporary music into the scene when they're editing it, and they're listening to it over and over and over again. And then when they go to tell the composer what they want, they're basically saying just make me this, but without the copyright issues. So that's definitely a huge restriction. They're not given any creative freedom.

ROSEMARY: Wait, what? This is so wild!

SH: So let's watch the clip that Julian posted on the discussion forum about this. [PLAYED CLIP]

KATE: I just wanted to share the question that I was thinking the entire time: Why hire a new composer if you [as a director] already know what you want? You know, it's like asking a question that you already know the answer to!

In this sample class discussion, I tried to mix up calling on *volunteers* with *cold calls* and *warm calls*. Cold calls are questions for students who may have difficulty answering them, but these questions can effectively get a student's attention or bring them into the conversation when they aren't volunteering. Warm calls are questions for students who I'm confident will be able to answer them, having read their discussion forum mini-essay. While this excerpt from the discussion is strong, several of my opening questions simply asked for recall of information. For example, I asked if anyone could define "Gesamtkunstwerk," or "Leitmotif." Asking for these definitions did not result in a good discussion, even when the students knew the answers. But when students felt free to express their own analysis, opinion, or evaluation, the class came alive and the students were speaking more to each other than to me.

The Opening Gambit

Case study instructors repeatedly stress the importance of the opening question, often urging professors not only to carefully prepare it but also to choose the student ahead of time to answer it and also, perhaps, the student who should follow up. When watching masterful case study instructors, both the opening question and the cold call ("Let's see …, uh, Kristen!") look spontaneous, though they are not.[11] Opening the class discussion with a question like, "What did you think of the reading?" will most likely result in an uncomfortable silence or, at best, responses that they either liked or disliked reading it, which is neither interesting nor stimulating.

Questions that don't elicit good responses are either

- too vague or too broad (students don't know how to address the subject, or don't know what is being asked)
- too difficult (students don't want to look stupid in front of their peers or their instructor)
- too indirect (students don't understand who is supposed to answer a question like "What did you all do over the weekend?")

A Better Sample Discussion

In the next example, the goal was to spark a hot debate from the very beginning. Context: the students read an article by the urban studies scholar Julia Foulkes that contrasts the histories of Lincoln Center and the Brooklyn Academy of Music after World War II.[12] The students also watched the film *The Opera House* that documents the construction of Lincoln Center.[13] I anticipated that asking the students to define "culture" would immediately open up a debate about the high/low art divide, which in the United States is coded by race, ethnicity, and class.

SH: Before we start our discussion I want to recognize that many of you feel really conflicted about Lincoln Center, and I do too. In many ways, Lincoln Center's a place that I love. I also want to recognize a tendency to paint things in strongly contrasting hues of "good" and "bad." It's easy to read this article and watch the movie and think that Lincoln Center is bad and the Brooklyn Academy of Music is good, in a very simplistic way. But of course it's far more complicated than that.

So my first question for this discussion is about Robert Moses, the city planner that advocated for slum clearance and the planning for Lincoln Center. He said that he wanted to make New York "a culture city for America." What does this mean? Cary, I'm going to ask you to give a swing at this one.

CARY: I don't know, I feel like there's different ways you can look at it. *I* feel like a culture city would be diverse, valuable to everyone in a way, and a place for everyone in the city.

SH: Do you think that's what Robert Moses had in mind?

CARY: I think if that was the true intent—that he wanted more culture and more diversity—then he would have left it alone. It was a neighborhood that was already adding culture and diversity, and it was destroyed to create a place where white, elitist culture was performed and celebrated. So I feel like the intent was not to create a culture city, but to spread more white culture and to, like, pretend that it was going to benefit everybody knowing that only certain people would be really able to go and be celebrated there.

SH: So you said culture was already there. What is "culture"?

CARY: Well, I look at it as like groups of people—different backgrounds, places, traditions, languages.

SOFIA: My opinions on this are very different from the rest of the class because for the first half of my life I grew up in New York City. I feel like what the article doesn't address is the changing climate of New York City, which could be hard to understand. I mean, the architecture, the neighborhoods, and rent prices. All of these things are constantly changing in the city. They are never constant, and they never have been constant. So I feel like to blame the construction of Lincoln Center on a changing neighborhood is wrong. Honestly, if Lincoln Center wasn't put there, something else would have been.

SH: I think your point about the changing city is a really good one. What I want you to do is to take a more critical look. You said if it hadn't been Lincoln Center, it would have been something else that replaced the neighborhood. So I want you to think specifically about *design* and the role that design plays in a changing city.

WILLOW: It's a question of, like, why did they choose to replace the neighborhood with something that did not directly serve the underrepresented communities that were replaced? I'm often in Lincoln Center and the architecture . . . it's *stunning*. It was made in a way that favored wealthier patrons and they made it difficult for people without automobiles, or money or, you know, social status to be involved. And even the author of the article spoke about the architecture, the fact that it was a plaza surrounded by roads that were hard as hell to cross. You know, there's also the whole idea of class separation inside the building with the seating and all of that fun stuff. Classism is directly integrated into the very essence of the building.

SH: Mateo, you wrote on your discussion forum post about how the San Juan Hill neighborhood was already a very rich cultural area. Could you explain more about that?

MATEO: Sure. I guess this goes back to the question you asked earlier about what even defines a cultural area and I guess on some level, it's kind of subjective. But I guess when we're talking about American culture, a lot of it derives from Black communities or communities of color, especially in this case, in New York. I talked about in my post how San Juan Hill was brimming with culture—jazz specifically. Kinds of jazz were said to have originated in the neighborhood. Thelonious Monk grew up there and of course he's a really well known jazz pianist.

SOFIA: So when we talk about how Lincoln Center replaced some jazz clubs in the city, I think it's important to remember that there are several prominent jazz clubs that still exist in Manhattan, but if Lincoln Center did not exist, there would be absolutely no opera in the city. So I think that's something to think about. A lot of people that do what we do, would not be able to do it if Lincoln Center did not exist.

While the previous discussion about film music covered more "material," this example engages the students more. I asked fewer questions and they made longer comments and spoke more to each other than to me. In fact, the conversation continued to be emotionally charged, putting students in the ideal place on the Yerkes-Dodson scale discussed in Chapter 1.

Starting every class in the same way, or trying to spark the same kind of controversial or contentious conversation, can become predictable. Be creative about the "opening gambit"; instead of always starting with a student's summary of the case or a controversial question, try starting with a quick quiz (like a Kahoot), poll, or prediction. You can also have students physically move from one side of the room to the other to form teams, or group them according to opinions or stances. You could have students generate questions for discussion at the beginning of class by writing them on a note card or sticky note. Students could brainstorm "facts" about the case quickly and collectively. Despite the fact that a case study discussion tends to put individuals on the spot, there are ways, such as "think-pair-share" or discussion in small groups, to support students so that they can test ideas before offering something to the entire class. A short freewriting exercise at the beginning of class can get *everyone* thinking about how to answer the opening question. In sum, don't let the opening gambit become predictable.[14]

If you get the first question for the class discussion right, then the rest of the class will flow from there. Your task then becomes that of a conductor: using your "roadmap" of key points as a guide, you "orchestrate" the discussion—deciding which voices to draw out, when to increase the tempo and dynamics, and when to insert a moment of reflection or repose. To bring up the energy level, you might move about the room, celebrate great answers and questions, and maybe even bring in props. Like every conductor, every professor has their own manner and demeanor. You will find your own style of guiding the discussion, but if I may state the obvious, students engage with engaging people. They will be enthused by your enthusiasm, and your curiosity will spark theirs.

White Board Strategy

In addition to the outline or "roadmap" and your opening question or activity, plan how you would like to use the boards in the classroom to take notes. Masterful case study teachers take notes on the board in such a way that students draw further conclusions from the information. Columns or categories are rarely labeled. Students sometimes have to work to identify what connects various elements within a section and how different sections of the board relate to one another; this is important interpretative, analytical, and evaluative cognitive work.

In the case study on Lincoln Center, I separated the board into two sections: one that defined culture inclusively and another that did so exclusively, or as "high art." In response to Cary's comment that culture includes "different backgrounds, places, traditions, languages," I wrote "difference, tradition, language" on the left side of the board. But when Isabella brought up the changing architecture of the city, I wrote "design" on the right side of the board. Willow picked up on the importance of this term and elaborated on design elements that were excluding. At the end of the class period, we came back to the key term, *design*, now surrounded by other terms that indicated the exclusive (and excluding) nature of many of the venues at Lincoln Center, but with a message of hope: if venues were designed to be exclusive, then we can challenge segregation, racism, misogyny, and ableism in the arts by creating a better design for the future.

Sample Opening Gambits and Board Strategies

Case Study	*Opening Question/Activity*	*Board Strategy*
Loren Kajikawa's article, "Possessive Investment in Classical Music"	How is our school of music like the theoretical one described in Kajikawa's article?	Three columns: (1) what is the same, (2) what is different, and (3) what students would like to see change
The experimental music of John Cage and the avant-garde jazz of the Art Ensemble of Chicago	Short written reflection: (1) define indeterminacy; (2) define improvisation. Open the discussion by comparing and contrasting definitions between students, drawing out problems in the two constructs.	Two columns: (1) indeterminacy and (2) improvisation. Note key terms on the board and then start to draw lines connecting elements common to both as they come up.
Beyoncé's *Lemonade*	What do we mean when we talk about style?	Two columns: (1) definitions that focus on individual attributes and (2) definitions that stress shared expectations. After exploring a general definition of style, we attempted to map the many styles represented on the album.

What Do Students Actually Learn During a Case Discussion?

It's fair to ask if case study discussions actually support student learning in music history courses. What is it that students are learning when they engage in debate with one another? Does a case study discussion support the student learning outcomes I identified in Chapter 1? At the end of the course, students will be able to

1 Demonstrate knowledge of cultural institutions and how they shape musical practices
2 Identify and describe significant stylistic features of a variety of musical practices throughout history
3 Engage in rigorous, open-minded, and creative inquiry regarding musical practices
4 Integrate multiple critical approaches to examine practical, artistic, and ethical issues related to music production and consumption
5 Locate, evaluate, and effectively use information to understand musical practices
6 Effectively express meaningful ideas about music in speech and writing

Discussions provide students opportunities to demonstrate knowledge––either knowledge of cultural institutions and historical events that have shaped musical practices or of significant stylistic features of the musical practices themselves. Because the students have to draw on facts and evidence in real time in the classroom, they are *using* the knowledge, not just repeating what they have memorized, as they might on an exam. As students react to primary and secondary sources in discussion, they are integrating multiple critical approaches. And the more they participate in classroom discussions, the more they learn to effectively express meaningful ideas about music. *Discussions encourage students to engage in rigorous, open-minded, and creative inquiry.*

The last exchange between Mateo and Isabella in the sample case study above is an excellent example of how discussion supports student learning. Mateo drew on his knowledge of musical contexts (the San Juan Hill neighborhood), styles (jazz history), and musicians (Thelonious Monk). Isabella evaluated information when she pointed out what the article does *not* address, and she made a polemical argument that despite the destruction of the San Juan Hill neighborhood, jazz still thrives in the city. Both students had to navigate a strong disagreement; they had to listen carefully to each other and advocate for their own ideas in a professional manner. Had the discussion gotten out of hand or personal, I would have paused the conversation and reminded the students of the discussion norms and expectations we created at the beginning of the semester. In a skillfully conducted case study discussion, students discover themselves as a member of a community of learners. They learn from one another, and the collective nature of the classroom can transform what they know and believe. They are also able to witness the skills, passion, and knowledge of the other students. A discussion of a case study allows students to draw from each other's strengths during debate and analysis. The power and energy of the discussion is then transferred to small group research projects, which is the focus of Chapter 5.

Notes

1 Epsen Andersen and Bill Schiano, *Teaching with Cases: A Practical Guide* (Boston: Harvard Business School Publishing, 2014), 49. Note that "boards" is plural because the ideal case study classroom has multiple, large, moveable boards.

2 Alexandra Sedlovskaya, "Building Inclusive Virtual Classrooms: Use the Four Cs Model to Encourage Tough Yet Necessary Discussions Among Students," *Harvard Business Publishing,* September 23, 2020, https://hbsp.harvard.edu/inspiring-minds/building-inclusive-virtual-classrooms

3 For more seating arrangement ideas with pros and cons for each, see Chris Drew, "12 Classroom Layout Ideas & Seating Arrangements," HelpfulProfessor.com, April 29, 2021, https://helpfulprofessor.com/classroom-layouts/

4 Andersen and Schiano, *Teaching with Cases*, 44.

5 Andersen and Schiano, *Teaching with Cases*, 51.

6 Andrew Farach-Colton, "Three Pioneers of Film Music: Shostakovich, Korngold and Copland," *Gramophone*, June 9, 2016, www.gramophone.co.uk/features/article/three-pioneers-of-film-music-shostakovich-korngold-and-copland

7 Sally Bick, *Unsettled Scores: Politics, Hollywood, and the Film Music of Aaron Copland & Hans Eisler* (Urbana, IL: University of Illinois Press, 2019), 11–23, 47–55.

8 For more on crafting a teaching plan, see Andersen and Schiano, *Teaching with Cases,* 52–54.

9 "The Marvel Symphonic Universe." YouTube, accessed November 27, 2021, www.youtube.com/watch?v=7vfqkvwW2fs

10 Farach-Colton, "Three Pioneers of Film Music."

11 Harvard Business School has sample videos available on YouTube. See, for example, "Take a Seat in the Harvard MBA Case Classroom," November 17, 2020, www.youtube.com/watch?v=p7iwXvBnbIE. The entire Harvard

Business School video playlist is available at www.youtube.com/channel/UCk8n46m74K5XWfdeBzOXDfA

12 Julia Foulkes, "Streets and Stages: Urban Renewal and the Arts After World War II," *Journal of Social History* 44, no. 2 (Winter 2010): 413–34.

13 *The Opera House,* directed by Susan Froemke (New York: Metropolitan Opera on Demand, 2017), streaming video.

14 Raymond C. Jones, "The 'Why' of Class Participation: A Question Worth Asking," *College Teaching* 56, no. 1 (Winter 2008): 61.

5   Student Inquiry and Project-Based Learning

Nietzsche claims that history is most often taught as a costly luxury, an overabundance of "facts," and that this approach enervates engagement in the world. He argues that we must "hate" such a pedagogical approach because it stands in the way of what we desperately need from a study of history. We need history, he wrote, for life and action.[1] A pedagogy that keeps learners passive is oppressive and alienating; to humanize learning is to make it active and collaborative.

In many disciplines, such as business, management, and law, a class discussion is a sufficiently active and empowering pedagogy as students collectively learn how to analyze and evaluate evidence in the context of a case study. In fields where the primary learning outcome is better decision-making, a case analysis—where students actively practice decision-making skills—is sufficient. The humanities are different. I argue that music history students, for example, need to learn and practice the skills specific to musicological inquiry and research; they should be able to ask a musicological question, collect data, and evaluate sources of information. While experts in the field usually do this kind of work alone, having students work in groups has added benefits. Not only do they learn and exercise musicological skills, but as they learn to work in groups they also develop transferable skills necessary for citizenship. Working in groups allows students to work from areas of strength, to advocate for one's own ideas, to navigate conflict, and to work collaboratively. Small group projects inspired by a case study allow students to actively *do* music history as they learn to formulate an original research question and to gather and evaluate information that will help them respond to their question.

In this chapter I discuss the benefits of teamwork and project-based assignments, and suggest that instructors can balance activities that stress "knowing" with those that require "doing." Figure 5.1 suggests that how much of a course is devoted to cognition-based work (case

DOI: 10.4324/9781003130482-5

Figure 5.1 Consider how much of a course is devoted to cognition versus active research and creation.

study readings and discussions) and how much is devoted to inquiry and project-based learning is adjustable; there may be reasons to tilt the curriculum or class in one way or another. I also describe in this chapter a variety of digital artifacts that students can create as teams and how they should guide their work with a research question. Finally, I discuss how to set up group work so that students are more likely to experience inner-group conflict in a productive manner, and how to—if necessary––mediate conversations with dysfunctional groups.

Why Small Groups?

In 2003, Peter Blatchford et al. wrote:

> In the future, the distinction between teacher and pupil, or expert and novice, may well become blurred, especially as information becomes more widely and instantly available. But learning is not just about information. The classroom of the future, and the pedagogy relevant to it, may be more about co-learners—that is, pupils learning from and with each other, and making sense of the information available to us all.[2]

That future is now! Pedagogical research since the 1990s has shown that group work is an effective strategy that can increase student engagement and retention, as well as increase the complexity of the materials and the level of challenge presented to students.[3] Cooperative, peer-to-peer learning increases opportunities for critical thinking and revision, and often offers a more realistic learning experience. The social benefits are also important as students build self-esteem, camaraderie, and leadership skills.[4]

The research on group work also notes that it requires strategic planning. It is essential for the instructor to create the groups intentionally, and to prepare students for collaborative work for the whole semester. Unfortunately, the elements that support successful group work, "are often unplanned and the 'social pedagogic' potential of classroom learning is therefore unrealized."[5] Instructors and students who are wary of group work express concerns about a loss of control, increased disruption and time wasted off task, and the inability of students to learn effectively from one another.[6] Students might fear that once in groups the strongest students will end up doing all the work and that their grades will be dragged down by the less capable or less invested students among them. These concerns can be mitigated with strategic planning, intentional development of students' cooperative skills, and thoughtful conflict resolution. When employed strategically, small groups can create opportunities for powerful peer-to-peer learning. Group learning is also an ideal pedagogical tool in a democratic classroom precisely because it exercises cooperative planning, monitoring, and evaluating skills.

For each student to be productive, the groups must be *small*. I have found that groups of 3–4 students work best. Groups must be *intentionally created* by the instructor; they should not be self-selected or selected randomly. Groups need to be *diverse* (a variety of majors, instruments/ voice types, genders, and ethnicities), and *balanced* (a variety of academic and interpersonal strengths, attitudes, and dispositions). The groups should also be *permanent*; that is, they should work together for the entirety of the semester.[7] Groups develop significant skills over time, and it is "important to give groups the opportunity to build up trust, sensitivity, and respect for each other, and to resolve conflicts through repeated opportunities to work and have fun together."[8]

It is essential that groups must define their own expectations and work methods. Before they begin work on a project, instructors should encourage them to explicitly define the following for themselves:

- **Purpose:** Why does this group exist? Why are group projects important for the learning process?
- **Goals:** What concrete outcomes do we intend to accomplish as a team? What level of quality do we expect from each other?
- **Roles:** Who will be responsible for what?[9] (Perhaps think of a film crew's defined roles: creative director, writer, actor, editor, technical director, etc.)

- **Agreement:** What do we expect from one another? What shared commitments do we want to put in place to ensure we function well? How will we share information, meet, and make decisions?
- **Support:** What kind of support (e.g., guidance, resources, information) do we need to succeed in achieving our purpose and objectives? Where can we find such support?[10]

It is useful to have students write a working agreement based on the questions above and to create a group name. Musicologist Andrew Granade has students also pick a theme song and choose an icon that will represent the group for the rest of the semester.[11]

Creating Group Work Assignments

Although I do occasionally give student groups directed assignments, I find the most productive group work is largely undirected. After a case discussion, I have groups collectively identify a question for further research and then execute a project. The question should be inspired by the case study, but I'm happy when students extend issues in the case to a wide variety of musical practices or contexts. I workshop the question with the groups, often urging them to narrow or refine the question, but I try to resist the urge to edit the question for them. Asking questions such as "What do you find attractive about this question?" or "What are you hoping to learn from this question?" will tease out a more productive or narrower focus. Students often find an appropriate focus for the question only after they begin researching. Even flawed questions are instructive, as students can reflect on what went wrong and learn from the experience (e.g., the question was too broad, ill-defined, or already thoroughly explored in the existing research). Even though I typically do not debrief with groups after projects, students almost always demonstrate a strong awareness of what went wrong in their self-reflections.

Students often identify a question or problem *before* they understand how they might have to go about answering it. The beauty of student-directed questions is that they often require a variety of different research methodologies. For example, in a study of camp aesthetics and queer identity, one group asked if hair bands from the 1980s, like Twisted Sister, were considered "camp." They decided that the best way to find out was to interview their relatives who would have been teens at that time. The ethnographic approach gave them great data, which then inspired them to turn to secondary research about heavy metal and performative masculinity. The nature of the question determined their research methodology.

Just as the topic and methodology are open, so is the project's form. While some groups create traditional class presentations with slides, others create projects ranging from original musical compositions, to works of visual art, lesson plans, children's books, intermedia skits, podcasts, timelines, and interactive maps. My broad definition of "project" is shaped by the four-pronged Boyer Model: *scholarship of discovery, scholarship of integration, scholarship of application,* and *scholarship of teaching and learning.*[12] In the Boyer model, a musical composition or work of visual art is a form of *creative inquiry* and is considered to be scholarship of discovery.

I give students a list of presentation ideas and resources at the beginning of the semester with the caveat that these are just suggestions. These project types work equally well in a face-to-face, hybrid, or online class. When classes are too large to have each group present in class, some presentations can be presented in class and the others shared online through the course management system.

Creative Project Ideas[13]

Book/Magazine: Create a children's book, mini-textbook, handbook, comic, or other kind of book. These can be done on paper or created with apps such as Book Creator, Canva, or Flipsnack.

Map Tour: Using an app like StoryMap, create customized tours that combine photos, text, and targeted locations. These could be used to create tours that explore the subject of your research question.

Infographic: On paper or using a tool such as Piktochart, create an infographic to represent or teach about an idea or set of data.

Lesson Plan: Write your own lesson plan on your research. Include objectives, direct instruction, guided practice, and some sort of assessment to measure success.

Museum or Multimedia Collection: Curate a collection of artifacts representing a topic or concept, along with written captions, in a Google Slides presentation. The Google Arts & Culture website can help you gather artifacts, as can many other primary source archives such as HathiTrust.

Podcast: Use simple recording tools (such as the recording app on your phone, tablet, or computer) or an app like Anchor to record a podcast.

Video: Create videos as creative, informative, persuasive, or reflective pieces. These can be performances, public service announcements, commercials, mini-documentaries, instructional videos, short feature films or animations, or TED-style talks. Tools for creating these can range from quick response platforms such as Flipgrid, to screencasting tools such as Zoom, a tool that creates stop motion videos such as Stop Motion Studio, or simple online video creators such as Adobe Spark or Acapella.

Website: Using tools such as Weebly, Wix, or Google Sites, develop a website to document a project or teach about a particular idea.

Annotated website: Host a collaborative conversation about existing web content using an annotation tool such as Perusall or Hypothes.is.

"Pop Up" video: Annotate a video by adding captions with an app such as iMovie.[14]

What about Cognitive Skills?

Some might argue that students doing group work that focuses on a narrowly defined project—as I'm suggesting—may develop collaborative work habits but will not develop the broader cognitive skills expected from traditional assignments and tests. Such an argument confuses the ability to memorize answers for a test with the cognitive skills of critical thinking, inquiry, and analysis. As I argue in Chapter 2, a content-centered—or what I called a "facts first"—approach to music history education is largely ineffective. Since facts (such as historical dates or specific details) are so easily accessible to students via rich online resources, the best way for students to study music history is to support their development of analytical and evaluative skills for contextualizing information. The ability to contextualize information is not just "more important or," on the same spectrum as facts, but *so much* more important that without this skill facts are meaningless or, worse, morally suspect. When we say, without context, that Guido d'Arezzo invented notation, we're saying something that's not only *inaccurate*, but immoral. The statement is inaccurate because it does not recognize notational traditions that pre-date Guido, and it's immoral because it excludes those practiced outside of the Western world.

Leon Botstein, president of Bard College, adds inquiry to the list of primary cognitive skills. According to Botstein, students "should know how to frame a question" and "should not be dependent on the sources of information, either provided by the government or by the media, but have an independent capacity to ask questions and evaluate answers."[15] In my article "From Answers to Questions: Fostering Student Creativity and Engagement in Research and Writing," I argue that centering research on an open question—rather than a topic— radically changes both the student's attitude to their work as well as their work habits. My research showed that for students that started their research with an open-ended question, the "quality, depth, and breadth of the research and writing improved dramatically." Focusing on inquiry gave students "a sense of ownership over their learning: they discovered that they were ultimately in charge of their own educational outcomes." They also started to understand that "the final product of their research should be an answer perhaps, but a provisional one, one that would be replaced by a more interesting and sophisticated question."[16]

According to educational psychologist Gregory Schraw, critical thinking skills such as inquiry and analysis can be taught under three conditions: (1) when students can observe experts in the field using such skills, (2) when students are given sufficient time to practice them in an authentic and meaningful context, and (3) when students can observe instances of the expert's own metacognition—their own reflective process on what they are doing and how well they are doing it.[17] Practicing musicians can easily grasp this three-pronged model because it likely mirrors their own experience: students need to hear outstanding performances by experts, they need to practice and play with others, and they need to learn how experts practice.

In a music history case study classroom, students observe expert work in the field as they read, study, and discuss the work of musicologists and other scholars. They are given sufficient time to practice musicological skills as they work collectively on their self-designed projects. Note that what is missing from Schraw's model is *critique of the student*. Schraw posits that access to an expert's own metacognition is more important than critique, and I will discuss this third prong of the model in Chapter 6 on assessment. Schraw's model may lead one to believe that the three conditions are steps in a sequential process, but they are not: the three conditions are iterative. A case study discussion allows students to observe and study expert musicological inquiry. And as students pose a research question and create a project, they are not only practicing musicological skills in a meaningful context, but they are also encountering more expert work as they do their own research.

Teaching Inquiry

For many students, it is not easy to acquire the skill of asking a good musicological question, especially since they have been conditioned from an early age to care primarily about the right answers. Most students of my generation who learned to frame a musicological question did so simply by acculturation or trial and error. I believe we can be much more intentional in the way that we teach inquiry.

First, I think it is important to give students a model for how to think about questions and introduce them to the scope and variety of perspectives that we employ when we ask musicological questions. In *Writing in Music: A Brief Guide,* my co-authors and I offer a list of types of questions musicologists ask:

- **Questions that establish facts:** Who/what/where/when questions work well to establish factual accounts of musical practices. Products of such studies include the creation of critical editions, repertory studies, archival studies, bibliographies, and biographies. These studies can create rich descriptions of historical contexts within which we can study specific practices. *Who participated in this musical practice? What instruments were employed? What musical works were produced? Where would such performances have taken place? When did this style emerge?*
- **"How" questions:** These questions explore issues associated with how to interpret musical styles or notations, or issues concerning practices, pedagogies, and technologies. *How would this musical practice have been performed? How was this musical practice taught, written, published, or recorded?*
- **Sociological questions:** These questions address the role(s) of music in society, including how music is created, received (reception history), performed, and used in everyday life. *How is meaning in music established or communicated? How closely does this musical practice reflect larger cultural practices or philosophical ideas?*
- **Intertextual questions:** Intertextual questions assume that all musical works are shaped by other works. We may hear in a piece similarities or allusions to other works. These questions address the ways that pieces are interconnected. *Does this musical work reference other works or styles through quotation or other means? What does it mean when a certain piece appropriates the style of another musical practice?*

- **Questions about identity:** Researchers asking these questions are interested in the experiences of groups of people defined by some aspect of their identity (race, ethnicity, language, gender, sexual orientation) or their experiences as a participant in a group (social, political, national, economic, or religious). Researchers focusing on the experiences of non-dominant groups draw on the philosophies of critical studies to frame their inquiry. *How does this musical practice represent aspects of identity? How does this musical practice contribute to the construction of identity?*
- **Cross-disciplinary questions:** Some research questions require scholars to draw from at least one other field to complement their disciplinary knowledge of music. Cross-disciplinary studies in music draw on philosophy, film studies, art history, literature, religious studies, anthropology, psychology, cognition, political science, economics, and ecology. *How does this musical practice work in tandem with this film, art installation, book, or poem? How does this musical practice relate to economic, political, power, and class structures? How does it relate to the sounds of nature and non-human animals?*[18]

Introducing students to the type and range of questions they might ask as they explore case studies in music history can help guide their process of inquiry.

Next, students can study or look for research questions in existing scholarly work. In addition to asking students to identify the research question in every article that they read to prepare for a case, at the beginning of the semester, I also have them read a set of opening paragraphs in order to identify the research question. I include examples that state the questions as such, as well as ones that don't include a question per se but clearly imply one. An excellent example of this type is Marc Vanscheeuwijck's article "Recent Re-evaluations of the Baroque Cello and What They Might Mean for Performing the Music of J. S. Bach."[19] The article opens with a historical definition of the "violoncello" that does not conform to our current one. Students can clearly discern the author's research question: given the variety of cello-like instruments, which instrument did Bach write for? Appendix 4 includes examples from published scholarship of clear research questions.

Research questions can also emerge from classroom discussions. For example, in a discussion of music during the plagues in the sixteenth and seventeenth centuries, a student asked if popular melodies associated with the plague were ever borrowed for cantus firmus or paraphrase masses. I find it important to pause the conversation at such moments to point out the quality of the question, even with a simple statement such as, "That's a great question for further research!"

Early in the semester, case-specific guided research activities can both model and promote inquiry. These activities are often an intermediate step between the case study discussion and the group's independent research. Once again, these activities encourage students to identify research questions in the existing literature, but they also demonstrate to them the kind and variety of research questions a musical topic can inspire. For example, when in my classes we study Beyoncé's *Lemonade* album, we discuss Robin James's book chapter from *The Lemonade Reader*.[20] The next class period, the students—in their small groups—select a different chapter from this collection of essays, read it in class, and give a very brief report of it to their classmates. I ask students to identify the following in their selected chapter:

1   Who is the author? What is their academic field or discipline? (e.g., religious studies, history, or black studies?)
2   What is the research question? Can you identify a thesis statement?
3   What is used as evidence or how is the argument being supported? (e.g., primary sources, secondary literature, or music-theoretical analysis?)
4   What is the author's conclusion? How would the author answer the question "So what?"

If each student in a group takes primary responsibility for one of the questions, then the group can collectively read the article, discuss their findings, then share their findings with the rest of the class—all within a 50-minute class period. What I value about this activity is that students see the wide variety of research questions that have been inspired by a single album and the variety of disciplinary lenses employed to engage the questions.

Over the course of the semester, these intermediary activities that prepare students for their independent work should become less prescribed. For example, instead of students selecting a chapter from a collection of essays that I've recommended, they can find an article or book chapter on their own, or select an artifact from a large digital collection and ask as many questions as possible about it. Table 5.1 demonstrates a shift from highly structured activities at the beginning of the semester to increasingly open, less structured ones.

Table 5.1 Sample intermediary group research projects for a music after 1900 class

Case Study	Preparatory Assignment	Guided Group Research Projects
Beyoncé's *Lemonade*	Robin James, "How Not to Listen to *Lemonade:* Music Criticism and Epistemic Violence"	Select a chapter from *The Lemonade Reader,* read, analyze, and discuss
Stravinsky's *Rite of Spring*	Tamara Levitz, "Racism at The Rite"[21]	Select a chapter of *The Rite at 100,* read, analyze, and discuss.
"Entartete Musik" ["Degenerate Music"]	Watch: "Art as Propaganda: The Nazi Degenerate Art Exhibit"[22] Read: "The Nazis' take on 'Degenerate Music'"[23]	Go to http://holocaustmusic. ort.org/politics-and-pro paganda/third-reich/entart ete-musik/ Explore the examples. Pick an example in the right-hand column labeled "Learn More" to report on.
Lincoln Center, the Arts, and Gentrification	Julia Foulkes, "Streets and Stages: Urban Renewal and the Arts After World War II"[24]	Explore one of the following digital archives, select an artifact to report on: NY Phil Met Opera BAM Jazz @ Lincoln Center Lincoln Center Groundbreaking (google arts & culture) NY Public Library NY City Municipal Archive NY Times Carnegie Hall
Experimentalism and the Art Ensemble of Chicago	John Cage, "Experimental Music," from *Silence,*[25] and Paul Steinbeck, "Introduction" to *Message to Our Folks.*[26]	Draw name of experimental artist out of a hat, research.
Camp Aesthetics	Mattijs van de Port, "Genuinely Made Up: Camp, Baroque, and Other Denaturalizing Aesthetics and the Cultural Production of the Real"[27]	Draw a decade after 1900 out of a hat and find an example of "camp" from that decade.

Group Work Examples

Given the opportunity to design their own research projects, students in my classes have done remarkable work. The following are examples of student questions and research projects inspired by case studies.

Beyoncé's "Becky with the Good Hair": Does Becky Have a Sound?

The group posing this question was inspired by the content they had encountered in the guided research exercise following the case study discussion. This group had read Janell Hobson's chapter "Getting to the Roots of 'Becky With the Good Hair' in Beyoncé's *Lemonade*."[28] Hobson is a women's, gender, and sexuality studies scholar, and the group was fascinated by her unpacking of how "hair is integral to identity, agency, and a more complicated racial consciousness."[29] When they were workshopping their question, I reminded them that they needed to bring their skills as musicians to this project. As a result they decided to ask if the character "Becky"—who appears throughout the album—is accompanied by a sonic marker.

After learning that "Becky" is hip-hop slang for a promiscuous white woman, one member of the group compiled references to Becky in hip-hop lyrics and another gathered country music lyrics that include the name Becky. They not only found a long and colorful use of the name in hip hop, but also an antithetical use of the name in country music. Comparing uses of the name in both styles and in *Lemonade,* the group concluded that Becky did *not* have a sonic marker; rather, by drawing on rich, historical black musical tropes throughout the album, Beyoncé sonically marked herself as *not white,* and, therefore, as *not Becky.*

I was impressed by how this group took a very simple question ("Does Becky have a sound?") as the starting place for sophisticated musical analysis and contextualization. I was surprised to hear them use the term "trope" in their presentation. This is a difficult term to explain to students if they lack an appropriate frame for it or have no need for the concept. The group had come across the term in their research, and it gave them a way to frame and make sense of the wide variety of historical Black musical styles present in Beyoncé's work.

How Did the Construction of Lincoln Center Influence the Creation of West Side Story?

While searching the digital archives of the New York Library for Performing Arts during a guided research exercise, this group found publicity photos for *West Side Story* taken on the streets of the soon-to-be-demolished San Juan Hill neighborhood. The musical is set in this neighborhood that is now the site of Lincoln Center, and condemned buildings and piles of rubble were used as sets in the *West Side Story* movie. The photos prompted the students to ask a number of questions: Why did Leonard Bernstein and Stephen Sondheim decide to set the musical in this neighborhood, knowing that it was slated for destruction? And what was Bernstein's role in the planning of Lincoln Center as the director of the New York Philharmonic? They also asked questions about musical appropriation of both Puerto Rican styles and jazz, especially in light of the rich musical history of the neighborhood. Finally, they asked about the role of nostalgia in this musical. What does a song like "Somewhere" mean in a setting that is no longer there? In their presentation, this group did not offer answers, but instead explored these rich questions and their implications.

During the Civil War, How Did Music from the Patriotic North and Rebellious South Differ from One Another?

In a case study on the use of music during wartime, this group was inspired to explore the differences between music used by Northern and Southern soldiers. They drew heavily on primary sources in the Civil War Sheet Music Collection at the Library of Congress in order to compare and contrast a number of songs and band compositions. While it was easy to find textual differences, they found that musical differences were difficult—if not impossible—to locate. In fact, they found evidence that music often brought the two sides together: both used drummers and buglers to signal the troops, both used bands for parades and ceremonies, and both the North and the South loved the same popular songs. The group presentation included a good number of scores and recordings from a variety of musical genres and styles to demonstrate their findings.

Mentoring Groups in Conflict

Evidence from student course evaluations suggests that the quality of the classroom experience is shaped primarily by the quality of the teamwork experience; that is, students who work well together have positive, transformative learning experiences, whereas those in dysfunctional groups are more likely to develop a negative attitude about the whole course. Mentoring groups in conflict was something that I have had to study and continue to practice. For me, this was the most challenging hurdle in the course redesign process.

It is important to understand that conflict at its core is not a bad thing. We can grow from conflict, and productive conflict in student groups can help clarify ideas, inspire deeper or more careful analysis, and help build interpersonal skills. Conflict can help students maintain the ideal balance between performance and engagement, as described in the Yerkes–Dodson model discussed in Chapter 1. Conflict is destructive, however, when it is avoided or is managed poorly.

Conflict—both productive and non-productive—can result from behaviors associated with various personality types. A "bullying leader" can create a competitive atmosphere by insisting on a specific research question or topic without collaborating with the rest of the group. The "bullying leader" can be quite destructive by belittling ideas from other group members or threatening them with a bad result or low grade if they don't go along. Conflict can also result from a "lone wolf" who never wants to participate in groups and is bitter about it, or an "overachiever" focused on the product instead of the process, or a "micromanager" who wants to divide up the work into independent parts and assign parts to group members.[30]

I have highlighted how each of these personality types can contribute to a dysfunctional group dynamic, but each type has a positive quality as well. "Bullying leaders" are, after all, leaders. A healthy leader can get the conversation started and recharge the group after a lull in activity. A lone wolf usually has a strong sense of integrity or creativity; this is a person who may want to "color outside the lines," so to speak. The "overachiever" will work hard to polish the group project. Finally, the "micromanager" can see projects in their constituent parts and delegate. These are all valuable skills, so it is helpful to see each type from both a "healthy" and "unhealthy" point of view.

While one might assume that the "bullying leader" causes the most conflict, students overwhelmingly report that their negative group experience was a result of someone who just didn't pull their weight in the group—what the pedagogue Curt Dommeyer calls a "social loafer."[31] When operating in an unhealthy manner, each of the personality types described above is ultimately trying to sidestep the challenge of collaboration, and each can cause other group members to disengage.[32] The phenomenon of social loafing is so pernicious that it warrants further discussion. It's important to see social loafing as less a cause of group dysfunction—as students often report—than it is a symptom of other problems. These can include (1) competitive or controlling group members, as described above, (2) insecurity about one's own ability to contribute quality work, (3) residual feelings from poor past group experiences, or (4) a student's diminished mental or physical wellbeing. Instructors can help mitigate conflict among competitive or controlling group members and help the social loafer productively reengage with the group. Students who are insecure about their own abilities often develop a stronger self-esteem if they can continue to work with their group. But, in my experience, diminished mental health is by far the most difficult obstacle. While some students report that the group experience supported them through a difficult season, others with severe depression and anxiety have had to find alternative work methods to complete the course. In fact, it was often their inability to work effectively in a group that alerted me to their struggles, so that even when students weren't able to complete the course I was able to help them find support services earlier in the semester than would have been the case in a typical lecture survey.

The following is a list of things instructors should do to ensure that groups can work to the best of their abilities, even groups with "bullying leaders," "lone wolves," "overachievers," "micromanagers," and "social loafers."

1 **Use peer evaluation as an assessment tool:** Team-based learning pedagogues Praveen Aggarwal and Connie O'Brien found that students were more likely to fully participate when groups were small (I suggest no more than five), when the scope of the project was limited (versus a semester-long project), and when grades were based on peer evaluation. Peer evaluations hold students accountable; without them, according to Aggarwal and O'Brien, "students are pretty much assured of getting the same grade as the rest of the group irrespective of the quality and quantity of their own contributions."[33] Make sure the peer evaluation rubric asks students to rate important aspects of the collaborative process: for example, cooperation, time on task, or kindness.[34] Better yet, have the class collectively create the rubric at the beginning of the semester. Focusing more on the quality of the process than the product will help mitigate bullying, overachieving, or micromanaging behavior. For longer projects, Aggarwal and O'Brien suggest multiple peer evaluations throughout the process so that group members have an opportunity to modify their behavior before it is too late.[35]

2 **Use self-assessment as a tool:** In addition to asking students to evaluate their peers, I ask them to give themselves points for each project using the same rubric they use for their peers. But more importantly, I ask them to *reflect* on the quality of their work and their collaborative process. A simple prompt such as "If you were going to do this project again, what would you do differently?"

helps students think about specific things they can do to be a more effective team member. Again, early and frequent reflection allows them to self-correct before it's too late.

3   **Give groups time to talk about their peer evaluations:** I do not share peer evaluation comments with students, but they do get an averaged peer review score. I then periodically set aside class time for students to have a frank conversation about their scores in their small groups. In such conversations, encourage them to shift their focus from what happened during the last project to what they can do better next time. These face-to-face communications are far more effective than written comments.

These conversations go surprisingly well. For example, an "overachiever" in one group was always shocked that she didn't get perfect scores from her teammates. When the group had a conversation about it, one group member said, "I don't believe in giving perfect scores because I can always see room for improvement. I also never give myself a perfect score." Once the "overachiever" understood her teammate's philosophy she was able to live with the slightly less-than-perfect peer evaluation score. Trust your students to be able to have these kinds of honest conversations; most students are eager to hear how they can work better together.

Group Mediation

Some groups may need a mediator to move forward. Make sure that your goal as a mediator is to help the students find a solution—not to give them one. Rather than prescribing solutions, try to steer the process with questions.

First, help students identify the source of the conflict. Social scientists have identified scarcity as the primary driver behind conflict, and while it may be specious to compare a student group's conflict to, say, peoples warring over diminishing water supplies, it can help to identify what they feel is scarce in the group's experience.[36] Typically, students in dysfunctional groups feel that their time is scarce and/or that their grade is threatened. Or students can feel that the group isn't hearing them or valuing their input. The resulting conflict in such situations can manifest around personalities, the subject content, or the work processes and can be exacerbated by diversity within the group, especially a group member's gender, cultural, or ethnic identity.[37] But simply identifying the scarcity (time, grade, or attention) can help alleviate the stress. Group members can then clarify expectations that will result in better time management, higher project scores, or better listening and communication skills. Have everyone in the group participate in the conversation about the nature of the conflict.

Giving students the vocabulary to speak of typical group roles (bullying leader, lone wolf, overachiever, micromanager, or social loafer) might help focus the conversation, but discourage them from name-calling. Encourage them to think about how we might take on one or more of these roles in groups. For example, instead of saying "Susan you are a lone wolf," say, "Susan, I feel like your role in this group might be the lone wolf."

Social loafing is pernicious because in the absence of communication or information we tend to fabricate what can be false stories to account for the loafer's behavior (e.g., "Jackson isn't here because he doesn't care about the class"). Ask, Why is the person absent or loafing? Then ask everyone in the group to report on how a group member's non-engagement affects them. These conversations can be transformative, that is, if the students are willing to be vulnerable with each other.

The Power of Vulnerable Communication

A super-senior returning to a junior-level course to graduate assumed that her group members were judging her for having failed the class the first time she took it. When she was absent from group meetings or disengaged, the group assumed that she didn't care about the class and that she didn't like working with them. In a mediated meeting, the super-senior admitted to the group that she felt ashamed and judged for having to retake the class, and that taking a single class on campus while working a full-time job was straining. The group was empathetic and rallied around her. The whole group dynamic changed, and instead of assuming she was intentionally blowing them off they worked out new meeting times and communication methods that worked better with her schedule.

Health care providers often encourage patients to develop what they call "Assertive Communication" skills because good communication ameliorates feelings of stress, resentment, anger, victimization, and revenge.[38] A common acronym that describes the qualities of assertive communication is "HARD": Honest, Appropriate, Respectful, and Direct. Passive or passive-aggressive communication is appropriate and respectful, but not honest or direct; and aggressive communication is honest and direct, but not appropriate or respectful. Assertive communication allows students to express what they think about a teammate's behavior and how it is affecting their ability to work as a team without accusing them. It can also allow students to share expectations that they have of each other that might help shape future work methods.

The X-Y-Z formula is a helpful tool: I feel X when you do Y in situation Z. Expressing how you *feel* gives the listener access to your inner experience. Placing those feelings in the context of the other's *behavior* in specific *situations* limits observations to the other's external expression. For both the speaker and the listener this formula can help students avoid speculating about the other's internal experience, feelings, or motivations. Such speculations are likely inaccurate and unhelpful and are likely to be met with resistance and even hurt feelings. Encourage students to use "I" statements and (if appropriate) to make eye contact.[39]

I feel X	when you do Y	in situation Z
I feel angry	when you are late	to our scheduled team meetings.
I feel insignificant	when you interrupt or talk over me	when I share ideas with the group.
I feel frustrated	when you miss the deadline for your part of the project	when we have to compile parts of our project before the due date.

Note in the examples above how the statements avoid name-calling or speculation about the other's motivations. Saying "I feel insignificant" is far more effective than saying "You are disrespectful."

The next step in the X-Y-Z process would be to make a direct request of the person: "I would like you to show up on time," or "I would like you to listen without interrupting," or "I would like you to turn in your part of the project before the deadline."

After encouraging students to request what they need to be productive as a group, ask them to recommit to working as a team. Try to keep them focused on future possibilities rather than past failings. If necessary, the group can create a contract that makes mutual expectations clear.

When mediating groups in conflict, remember that an important outcome of this process is their learning to work productively in groups. Trust the process and the students' ability to navigate these difficult situations. Trying to avoid conflict and the discomfort it may cause by fixing the problem for them undercuts their growth. Remember, students can learn significant skills for resolving conflicts only by working through the difficulties themselves.

Group Diversity: Friend or Foe?

I recommend above that instructors create groups that are diverse, and yet diversity within a group can cause or exacerbate conflict. One way to mitigate conflict sparked by gender, ethnic, racial, or cultural differences is to start with subject matter that is also diverse. Using cases with a variety of examples, situations, and protagonists will automatically create a more inclusive atmosphere for the groups as they embark on their own research projects. Modeling inclusivity in class discussions by being intentional about who gets to speak may help diverse groups hear and value different points of view.

Studies show that diverse teams are initially less effective than non-diverse ones. Researchers Warren Watson et al. found that diverse teams initially spend more time solving interpersonal problems, but that by the end of the semester they performed better than non-diverse teams. In fact, the "differences in cultural characteristics were predictive of team scores," precisely because these groups enjoyed an "advantage of having ethnically different views for team problem-solving." These differences "resulted in higher team performance after the teams learned how to utilize these differences to their benefit."[40] Often, the primary factor that determines how students feel about working in groups is connected to how they are assessed as a team, and that discussion is continued in Chapter 6.

Notes

1 Friedrich Nietzsche, *Unzeitgemässe Betrachtungen: Zweites Stück: Vom Nutzen und Nachtheil der Historie für das Leben* (Leipzig: E. W. Fritzsch, 1874), iii–iv. Author's translation.
2 Peter Blatchford, Peter Kutnick, Ed Baines, and Maurice Galton, "Toward a Social Pedagogy of Classroom Group Work," *International Journal of Educational Research* 39, nos. 1–2 (2003): 169.
3 Graham Gibbs, "The Assessment of Group Work: Lessons from the Literature," *Assessment Standards Knowledge Exchange,* Centre for Excellence in Teaching and Learning in Higher Education, The Business School, Oxford Brookes University, (December 2009): 1, https://neillthew.typepad.com/files/groupwork-gibbs-dec-09.pdf
4 Praveen Aggarwal and Connie O'Brien, "Social Loafing on Group Projects: Structural Antecedents and Effect on Student Satisfaction," *Journal of Marketing Education* 30, no. 3 (December 2008): 256.

5 Blatchford, et al., "Toward a Social Pedagogy of Classroom Group Work," 153.

6 Blatchford, et al., "Toward a Social Pedagogy of Classroom Group Work," 157.

7 Much of this structure is similar to Team Based Learning (TBL). See Jim Sibley and Peter Ostafichuk, *Getting Started with Team-Based Learning* (Sterling, VA: Stylus, 2014).

8 Blatchford, et al., "Toward a Social Pedagogy of Classroom Group Work," 165–166.

9 Some instructors find it useful to assign group roles. I would rather have students self-identify their strengths and use them in group work.

10 Adapted from Carpenter Strategy Toolbox, "Charting a Path to Effective Project Teams," November 17, 2018, https://carpenterstrategytoolbox.com/2018/11/17/team-charters/

11 Andrew Granade, personal communication, January 27, 2022.

12 Ernest L. Boyer, "From Scholarship Reconsidered to Scholarship Assessed," *Quest* 48 (1996): 131–132.

13 Adapted from Jennifer Gonzalez, "Distance Learning: A Gently Curated Collection of Resources for Teachers," *Cult of Pedagogy,* March 30, 2020, www.cultofpedagogy.com/distance-learning/

14 Lacie Eades, "Encountering Western Classical Music with a 1990's VH1 Twist: Creating a Pop-Up Video Assignment," Teaching Music History Conference, June 17, 2020.

15 Leon Botstein quoted in Kate Zernike, "Tests Are Not Just for Kids," *New York Times*, August 4, 2002, www.nytimes.com/2002/08/04/education/tests-are-not-just-for-kids.html

16 Sara Haefeli, "From Answers to Questions: Fostering Student Creativity and Engagement in Research and Writing" *Journal of Music History Pedagogy* 7, no. 1 (2016): 2, 11.

17 Gregory Schraw, "Promoting General Metacognitive Awareness," *Instructional Science* 26 (1998): 122–123.

18 Lynne Rogers, Karen Bottge, and Sara Haefeli, *Writing in Music: A Brief Guide* (Oxford: Oxford University Press, 2020), 27–28.

19 Marc Vanscheeuwijck, "Recent Re-Evaluations of the Baroque Cello and What They Might Mean for Performing the Music of J. S. Bach." *Early Music* 38, no. 2 (2010): 181.

20 Robin James, "How Not to Listen to *Lemonade:* Music Criticism and Epistemic Violence," in *The Lemonade Reader: Beyoncé, Black Feminism and Spirituality*, Kinitra D. Brooks and Kameelah L. Martin, eds, 69–76 (New York: Routledge, 2019).

21 Tamara Levitz, "Racism at the Rite," in *The Rite of Spring at 100,* Severine Neff et al. eds., 146–180 (Bloomington, IN: Indiana University Press, 2017).

22 Jonathan Petropoulos, "Art as Propaganda: The Nazi Degenerate Art Exhibit," *Facing History and Ourselves,* accessed July 7, 2020, www.facinghistory.org/resource-library/video/art-propaganda-nazi-degenerate-art-exhibit

23 "The Nazis' take on 'Degenerate Music'" *Deutsche Welle,* accessed July 7, 2020, www.dw.com/en/the-nazis-take-on-degenerate-music/a-16834697

24 Julia L. Foulkes, "Streets and Stages: Urban Renewal and the Arts After World War II," *Journal of Social History* 44, no. 2, (Winter 2010): 413–434, www.jstor.org/stable/25790364

25 John Cage, "Experimental Music," in *Silence,* 7–12 (Hanover, NH: Wesleyan University Press, 1973).

26 Paul Steinbeck, "Introduction," in *Message to Our Folks,* 1–8 (Chicago: University of Chicago Press, 2017).

27 Mattijs van de Port, "Genuinely Made Up: Camp, Baroque, and Other Denaturalizing Aesthetics and the Cultural Production of the Real," *The Journal of the Royal Anthropological Institute* 18, no. 4 (December 2012): 864–883, www.jstor.org/stable/23321454

28 Janell Hobson, "Getting to the Roots of 'Becky With the Good Hair' In Beyoncé's *Lemonade,*" in *The Lemonade Reader: Beyoncé, Black Feminism and Spirituality,* Kinitra D. Brooks and Kameelah L. Martin, eds, 31–41 (New York: Routledge, 2019).

29 Hobson, "Getting to the Roots of "Becky with the Good Hair," 40.

30 Names for types of group members such as "micromanager" or "lone wolf" are ubiquitous through the scholarly literature on group work efficacy. S. B. Channon et al. identified the following rolls: Shaper (task-focused, energetic, achiever), Chairperson (confident, stable, and mature; a delegator), Plant (creative, unorthodox, generator of ideas), Team worker (good listener, diplomat), Monitor evaluator (fair, logical, strategic, impartial observer), Resource investigator (outwardly focused, outgoing, networker; rigorously pursues contacts and opportunities), Completer (perfectionistic, high standards), Company worker (efficient, disciplined; turns ideas into positive action). See S. B. Channon, R. C. Davis, N. T. Goode, and S. A. May, "What Makes a 'Good Group'? Exploring the Characteristics and Performance of Undergraduate Student Groups," *Advances in Health Sciences Education* 22, no. 1 (March, 2017): 17–41. http://dx.doi.org/10.1007/s10459-016-9680-y

31 Curt Dommeyer, "Using the Diary Method to Deal with Social Loafers on the Group Project: Its Effects on Peer Evaluations, Group Behavior, and Attitudes," *Journal of Marketing Education,* 29, (2007): 175.

32 Aggarwal and O'Brien, "Social Loafing on Group Projects," 256.

33 Aggarwal and O'Brien, "Social Loafing on Group Projects," 262.

34 For several sample peer evaluation rubrics, see Chad Manis, "Cooperative Learning Evaluation Instruments," *Daily Teaching Tools,* accessed February 23, 2022, www.dailyteachingtools.com/cooperative-learning-evaluate.html #SelfEvaluation

35 Aggarwal and O'Brien, "Social Loafing on Group Projects," 262.

36 A foundational article on scarcity and conflict is T. N. Carver, "The Basis of Social Conflict," *American Journal of Sociology* 13, no. 5 (March 1908): 628–648.

37   Andrey Sidorenkov, Evgueni Borokhovski, and Viktor Kovalenko, "Group Size and Composition of Work Groups as Precursors of Intragroup Conflicts," *Psychology Research and Behavior Management* 11 (September 2018): 514, 519, www.dovepress.com/group-size-and-composition-of-work-groups-as-precursors-of-intragroup--peer-reviewed-fulltext-article-PRBM

38   "Being Assertive: Reduce Stress, Communicate Better," *Mayo Clinic,* May 29, 2020, www.mayoclinic.org/healthy-lifestyle/stress-management/in-depth/assertive/art-20044644

39   Some students, especially those who have autism spectrum disorders find eye contact extremely difficult. See Rozella Stewart, "Should We Insist on Eye Contact with People Who Have Autism Spectrum Disorders," Indiana Resource Center for Autism, Indiana University, (accessed February 11, 2021), www.iidc.indiana.edu/irca/articles/should-we-insist-on-eye-contact-with-people-who-have-autism-spectrum-disorders.html

40   Warren Watson, Lynn Johnson, and George Zgouridesc, "The Influence of Ethnic Diversity on Leadership, Group Process, and Performance: An Examination of Learning Teams," *International Journal of Intercultural Relations* 26 (2002): 14.

6 Assessment in the Case Study Classroom

When I moved from a lecture survey to a case study approach to music history, I radically rethought assessment—especially its purpose and outcomes. My conclusion was that tests (I was giving three per semester) were likely measuring the students' skills at taking tests and not their knowledge of music history, their aptitude, or growth over the semester. I was frustrated when, reviewing for tests, students would ask questions such as "For the multiple-choice questions, will there be four or five options to choose from?" I found that students were strategizing about how to navigate the test rather than diving into the rich and engaging materials I'd offered them. Students were thinking strategically, I later learned, because I had set them up to do so with the structure of the course. They were motivated to do well, and I appreciated that, but their focus was on the test score and not on the subject matter. During my first year of teaching at my present institution, students complained on course evaluations that I didn't care about their grades, and they were correct! But they cared about their grades a great deal because for many their GPAs were tied to their merit scholarships, and if they were to fail to maintain a high average they would be in danger of losing that financial support and with it their ability to continue studying at their college of choice.

I decided that one way to get students to stop focusing on their grade was simply to *stop grading them*. Instead of assessing them with various quizzes and tests, I switched to a system in which the students assess their own learning. I replaced the old assessment tools with group work and writing or creative assignments that were graded by self-assessment and peer evaluation. I wanted them to be working not for me or for my approval, but for themselves and each other. This shift in assessment resulted in lower student stress and anxiety levels and better attendance. Their work was more creative, riskier, and often went beyond what was

DOI: 10.4324/9781003130482-6

expected in both depth and breadth. They were showing up in new and energetic ways that I had not seen before, and often *for each other*.[1]

In this chapter, I introduce the idea of *ungrading*. Keep in mind that, even in an ungraded class, students at most institutions will still receive grades at the end of the semester. The difference is that instead of an assessment from the instructor the grades in this case are based on completion of assignments, contract grading, self-assessment, or peer evaluation. I understand that many instructors may not be in a position to abandon traditional assessment methods, and for those I offer alternative ways to assess case study work beyond the typical music history exam.

Ungrading Strategies

Limited Grading

I suggested that one way to begin to teach with cases was to start by replacing just a few lectures with a few case studies; the same strategy applies to ungrading. Instead of going completely gradeless, consider making some assignments grade free—especially lower stake ones. Ungrading advocate Jesse Strommel suggests creating "grade free zones" for, say, the first third of the semester or for certain types of assignments.[2] Replace the grade for such assignments with a peer- or self-evaluation, or instructor feedback, or no feedback at all. Perhaps these assignments (such as freewriting) wouldn't even be turned in.

A second limited grading strategy also could include using fewer gradations in the grading scale. Instead of the five gradations of the traditional A–F system, or the eleven gradations (if one adds in plusses and minuses), the writing pedagogue Peter Elbow suggests minimizing the grade scale:

- Three levels: strong/satisfactory/weak, or excellent/OK/no credit.
- Two levels: pass/fail, satisfactory/no credit, or check/minus.
- One level: the assignment is acceptable if it is simply turned in.[3]

I have used all three scales suggested by Elbow to assess discussion forum posts and have found that the quality of the discussion did not change. It seems that students are not motivated by the extra points that separate a "strong" post from a "satisfactory" one; in fact, many are simply confused by the distinction between the two gradations, even with what I consider to be a clear rubric. I prefer the "one level" scale for individual work such as discussion forum assignments. For example, I describe how I have students prepare for discussion by writing about the case on the learning management system in Chapter 3. I grade these discussion forum posts as complete/incomplete.

Self-Assessment and Peer Evaluation

Self-assessment represents an indication of trust in the student; that is, a trust that students—and not instructors—are best equipped to report on their own learning and growth. I've already noted the power of self-assessment and peer evaluation to help mitigate social loafing and other unproductive group behaviors, and I have noted the role of self-assessment in building metacognition. Here, I offer some practical guides to both.

After every group project, I ask students to reflect on and assess their own work and the work of their teammates.[4] In the example below, note the balance between the work that was done and a reflection on how to do better going forward. The self-assessment and peer-assessment ask about the past process and product, but with an eye toward future improvement and better teamwork.

Sample Student Project Assessment

This example is from a case study framed by the question, "How did people learn music in the Baroque period?" The students read Curtis Price's article "Dido and Aeneas: Questions of Style and Evidence" and Ellen Rosand's article "Vivaldi's Stage."[5] For their project, the group created a skit of an orientation session for interested parents and students at the St. Thomas school during J. S. Bach's tenure at the institution. The skit described life at the school—including a description of the students' diet—music theory and vocal training, religious education, and general disciplinary methods.

What was your research question for this project?
    What was the role of music education in Lutheran schools in the early eighteenth century?
Briefly describe your contribution to the case study and presentation:
    I proposed the skit as the presentation format, I researched music education in Baroque Germany and J. S. Bach's involvement with the St. Thomas school, and I contributed to the script writing. I also played a killer orientation leader in our skit.

If you were to do this project again, what would you do differently?
I wish we had discovered the effectiveness of Google Docs for our group's working style sooner! We tried a few modes of communication, including texting and emails, and they didn't have great success with our group. With the Google Doc we made for the St. Thomas School project, we were able to define our research question and assign roles, share summaries of the articles we read, and work collaboratively on the script, all in one central place.

How could your group work together more effectively next time?
Keep using Google Docs! It was seriously a game-changer. We are beginning to discover our strengths in group work—Alec is good at tech, Caroline is a great actor, Jesse is great at keeping us focused and asking clarifying questions—and I think we need to keep discovering what we are all good at and using that to our advantage.

I then ask students to rate their teammates using a 1–5 point scale on a rubric.[6] I have had classes create their own rubric based on what they value in group work. Surprisingly, those differ from Table 6.1 in detail only; the large-scale ideas are almost always present.

Table 6.1 Self-assessment and peer evaluation rubric

Values: 5=Superior 4=Above Average 3=Average 2=Below Average 1=Week

Group Member Name	[self]	[member 1]	[member 2]	[member 3]
Participated in discussions				
Stayed on task				
Contributed quality work, creative ideas				
Was considerate of others				
TOTALS				

Grading Case Study Work

Not all educators are convinced by these arguments for ungrading, and for many the idea that students will show up to class prepared for deep

discussion simply because they are internally motivated seems ideal-
istic and naïve. Case-based pedagogy experts Andersen and Schiano
find that the demands of other classes, work, and life can all too easily
take precedence over case study preparation unless there is a concrete
external incentive—like a grade—to motivate the work. But Andersen
and Schiano concede that grading is hard work that requires careful
design and that there must be "a direct link between what the students
do during and after the course and the grades they end up with."[7]
Consider the following questions as you think about how to grade:

1   How much of a student's grade should be based on in-class partici-
     pation? Could participation be measured in other ways as well, such
     as online discussion forums?
2   How much of a student's grade should be based on group work?
     How much on individual work?
3   What kind of assessment tools should be used to measure mastery
     of the materials, skill acquisition, and growth over the semester?

Participation Grades

Schiano does not typically have students write about a case study before
every class discussion, as I do. Instead, he grades participation in class
by replaying the discussion in his memory immediately after class and
noting who spoke. He assesses whether or not students are prepared for
both "warm calls" (when students raise a hand to participate in the discussion or are given advance notice of leading part of the discussion)
and "cold calls" (when students are called on without raising a hand).
Andersen and Schiano recommend that between 30 and 50 percent of
a student's final grade should be based on participation.[8] For students
with extreme social anxiety, this kind of high-stakes class discussion
can trigger a panic attack. Schiano works with the students' therapists
"to treat speaking in class as an *in vivo* exposure where the students
would apply techniques they learned in therapy (breathing, reframing
thoughts, and so on) to manage their anxiety."[9]

Andersen and Schiano's grading practice is common, but studies
have shown that grading a student based on the number of times they
speak in class is problematic. First, most instructors rely solely on
their memory, which can be faulty or biased.[10] Second, students that
represent a minority in the classroom (typically women and students
of color, but not exclusively) are often reluctant to participate.[11] Third,
instructors don't often explain how participation is being graded, so
students are confused about what is required of them. Fourth, students
may assume that participation is a factor of the *quantity* of their verbal

contributions to the discussion and not the *quality*.[12] Sociologist Alanna Gillis recommends that instead of "assuming that students have sufficient skills to participate equally, instructors can incentivize and assess how well students improve their participation skill set over the course of the semester."[13] Gillis suggests that focusing on skill-building encourages students to see participation as something that can be developed and not just a result of something that is determined by their personality. Gillis breaks participation into five aspects:

1   **Attendance and tardiness:** coming to class every day, being on time, and not leaving early.
2   **Preparation for each class meeting:** completing readings, taking notes, reviewing quiz questions.
3   **Participation in small group discussions:** actively sharing thoughts, listening to group members and considering their perspectives, being respectful, and remaining on task.
4   **Participation in full class discussions:** actively sharing thoughts, listening to classmates and considering their perspectives, being respectful, and remaining on task.
5   **Participation in other ways:** a variety of activities including but not limited to attending office hours, going to the writing center, using working groups, peer editing papers with a partner, and discussing course material outside of class with peers or friends.[14]

Gillis has students report at the beginning of the semester on how well they typically perform in each of the participation aspects. Students then set goals for three to five of the aspects and create a plan (a full paragraph of text) about how they intend to achieve the goal. Gillis then relies on periodic quantitative and qualitative self-reporting to determine participation grades. Students are encouraged to adjust goals if necessary in light of their own reflection and instructor feedback. Gillis finds that "students came to realize that speaking in class—in small or full class discussions—is indeed a skill."[15] Students discover that once they had begun to work on a skill, like speaking in class, participating got much easier, and that improvement in one aspect of participation carried over to others; for example, working on speaking in class improved class preparation.

Exams

An exam should test the skills and knowledge that students have acquired over the semester, and if you have adopted a case study approach, then the exam should also be case-based. For example, students could work with a relatively short primary source, article, or blog post as the material for a case study analysis during the exam period. The students would read the case during the exam period and then answer two to three questions that require skills learned during the semester, including their ability to summarize, assess, evaluate, and apply the information presented in the case. Alternatively, you could give the students a longer, more complicated case to study *before* the exam period and then have them write the exam in class, or even give them a longer take-home exam; the take-home exam has the added benefit of measuring how students could extend the issues presented in the case to a nascent and original research question and project.

Concluding Thoughts on Assessment

I suggested in Chapter 1 that we might think of students as "ice cubes," and that learning is a process one of "melting" and "refreezing." The outcomes in an "ice cube" model are going to be unique to each student. It may feel more comfortable for both instructors and students to treat learning as a standardized process, like filling a "bucket," and assessment as a simple act of measuring the fullness of the bucket. What is lost in standardized assessment is the ability to recognize and reward the variability of classroom experiences and outcomes, all of which may be deeply enriching for the student. It is also difficult to measure valuable "soft" skills such as creativity, teamwork, decision-making, communication, and grit. How we assess students is an indication of what we value in the learning process and to what degree we have made students partners in the experience.

Notes

1 There is a large body of research that attests to the importance of friendships to academic success. See, for example, Christoph Stadtfeld, et al., "Integration in Emerging Social Networks Explains Academic Failure and Success," *PNAS: Proceedings of the National Academy of Sciences of the United States of America* 116, no. 3 (January, 2019): 792–797, https://doi.org/10.1073/pnas.1811388115

2 Jesse Strommel, "How to Ungrade," in *Ungrading: Why Rating Students Undermines Learning (and What to Do Instead)*, edited by Susan D. Blum, (Morgantown: West Virginia Press, 2020), 36.

3 Peter Elbow, "Grading Student Writing: Making It Simpler, Fairer, Clearer," *New Directions for Teaching and Learning* 69 (Spring 1997): 128.

4   Strommel calls a written reflection for a substantial assignment a "process letter"; he also suggests as an alternative to a written reflection that students could curate a collection of photos of the work as it evolved, record a voice over screen cast, or make a "behind the scenes" video. Strommel, "How to Ungrade," 37.

5   Curtis Price, "Dido and Aeneas: Questions of Style and Evidence," *Early Music* 22, no. 1, (February 1994): 115–122, 124–125; and Ellen Rosand, "Vivaldi's Stage," *The Journal of Musicology* 18, no. 1 (Winter 2001): 8–30.

6   "Cooperative Learning Evaluation Instruments," *Daily Teaching Tools,* accessed January 4, 2020, www.dailyteachingtools.com/cooperative-learning-evaluate.html#SelfEvaluation

7   Epsen Andersen and Bill Schiano, *Teaching with Cases: A Practical Guide* (Boston: Harvard Business School Publishing, 2014), 112, 113.

8   Andersen and Schiano, *Teaching with Cases,* 113.

9   Andersen and Schiano, *Teaching with Cases,* 152.

10   Tina Opie, Beth Livingston, Danna Greenberg, and Wendy Murphy, "Building Gender Inclusivity: Disentangling the Influence of Classroom Demography on Classroom Participation," *Higher Education* 77, no. 1 (2019): 37+.

11   John Wesley White, "Resistance to Classroom Participation: Minority Students, Academic Discourse, Cultural Conflicts, and Issues of Representation in Whole Class Discussions," *Journal of Language, Identity, and Education* 10 (2011): 250–265.

12   Alanna Gillis, "Reconceptualizing Participation Grading as Skill Building," *Teaching Sociology* 47, no. 1 (January 2019): 10–11, https://doi.org/10.1177/0092055X18798006

13   Gillis, "Reconceptualizing Participation Grading as Skill Building," 13.

14   Gillis, "Reconceptualizing Participation Grading as Skill Building," 14.

15   Gillis, "Reconceptualizing Participation Grading as Skill Building," 16.

Appendix 1: Sample Course Schedules

Table A.1.1 Music History (1600–1800)

Case Study	*Homework Assignment*
Is Music History racist?	Read Chapter 7: "Possessive Investment in Classical Music: Confronting Legacies of White Supremacy in U.S. Schools and Departments of Music" by Loren Kajikawa, in *Seeing Race Again: Countering Colorblindness Across the Disciplines*
What do we mean when we call a composer a "genius?" and other music historical problems	Read the following posts by Sara Haefeli from *The Avid Listener* blog: 1. "If History Is Written by the Victors" 2. "The Problem with Geniuses" 3. "Does Music Evolve?"
What role can music play during a time of crisis?	Watch: "Passamezzo—Lord Have Mercy Upon Us" by Angel Early Music (YouTube video) Explore: *Songs in Times of Plague*
What is a Castrato? And *WHY?*	Read: Roger Freitas, "The Eroticism of Emasculation: Confronting the Baroque Body of the Castrato"
How did people learn music in Europe during the Baroque period?	Pick one to read: 1. Curtis Price, "Dido and Aeneas: Questions of Style and Evidence" 2. Ellen Rosand, "Vivaldi's Stage" 3. Marie Stultz, "Performing Dido and Aeneas with Adolescent Singers: Purcell's Original Commission"
Can music represent political power?	Read Chapter 21: "Lully: The King Is Dancing" in *The Meaning of Music* by Leo Samama

(continued)

Table A.1.1 Cont.

Case Study	Homework Assignment
How did colonialism shape music-making practices?	Read Chapter 1: "Colonialism in Indonesia: Music Moving with an Occupying Force" in *Music on the Move* by Danielle Fosler-Lussier
Are drums weapons?	Read: "Narratives of Musical Resilience and the Perpetuation of Whiteness in the Music History Classroom," by Travis Stimeling and Kayla Tokar
How can music represent something that isn't music?	Read Chapter 1: "From Rhetoric to Semiotics" in *Mozart and Enlightenment Semiotics* by Stephen Rumph
Why do we make composers into gods and legends?	Read this web article and watch several of the example videos: "In-depth Carnatic Primer: South India's Mellifluous, Mathematical Music," by George Howlett (www.darbar.org/article/carnatic-primer)
What does musical notation actually signify?	Read: "Cracking the Code: What Notation Can Tell Us About Our Musical Values," in *Open Access Musicology,* by S. Andrew Granade
	Watch: *Awake My Soul: The Story of the Sacred Harp* (documentary film)

Table A.1.2 Music and the Media

Case Study	Homework Assignment
Sheet music	1. Read: "Tin Pan Alley Was Where the Publishing Industry in the US Was Born," *The Music Origins Project,* www.musicorigins.org/item/tin-pan-alley-was-where-the-publishing-industry-in-the-us-was-born/
	2. Explore: "Tin Pan Alley Sheet Music Collection," Digital Collections, University of South Carolina Libraries, https://digital.library.sc.edu/collections/tin-pan-alley/
Recording and listening technologies	Pick one from Mark Katz, *Capturing Sound: How Technology Has Changed Music*:
	Chapter 2: "Making America More Musical: The Phonograph and 'Good Music'"
	Chapter 3: "Capturing Jazz"
Radio	Read Chapter 33: "Radio and the Foundation of American Broadcasting, by John Wright, in *American Mass Media: Industries and Issues,* edited by Robert Atwan, Barry Orton, William Vesterman

Table A.1.2 Cont.

Case Study	Homework Assignment
Film	1. Read/Watch: "Three pioneers of film music: Shostakovich, Korngold and Copland," by Andrew Farach-Colton, www.gramophone.co.uk/features/article/three-pioneers-of-film-music-shostakovich-korngold-and-copland 2. Listen: "Batman: The Music (1989)" *The Soundtrack Show* (podcast) https://podcasts.apple.com/no/podcast/batman-the-music-1989/id1351960656?i=1000454647350 3. Watch: "The Marvel Symphonic Universe," www.youtube.com/watch?v=7vfqkvwW2fs&t=349s
Television	1. Read Chapter 1: "The CBS Stock Music Library and the Reuse of Cues" in *A Dimension of Sound: Music in the Twilight Zone* by Reba Wissner 2. Watch: "The History of MTV," www.youtube.com/watch?v=Y6jz65YRCy8
Advertising	1. Read: "Classical Music in Television Commercials: A Social-Psychological Perspective," by Peter Kupfer 2. Read Chapter 5: "The Standardization of Jingle Production in the 1950s and After," in *The Sounds of Capitalism: Advertising, Music, and the Conquest of Culture,* by Timothy D. Taylor
Personal listening devices	1. Read Chapter 2: "The World of Personal Stereo Users: An Introduction," in *Sounding Out the City: Personal Stereos and the Management of Everyday Life,* by Michael Bull 2. Read: "'Hear What You Want': Sonic Politics, Blackness, and Racism-Canceling Headphones," by Alex Blue V.
Internet	Read: "Beyoncé" (case narrative from Harvard Business Publishing)
Video games	1. Read Chapter 7: "Gameplay, Genre, and the Functions of Game Audio," in *Game Sound: An Introduction to the History, Theory, and Practice of Video Game Music and Sound Design,* by Karen Collins 2. Watch: "Brief History of Game Music," www.youtube.com/watch?v=wyD_4niwIs4 3. Play: Any video game, taking note of how the music is shaping your experience

Appendix 2: Sources for Case Study Materials

Chapter 3 includes a discussion of various sources for case study readings beyond scholarly publications, including open access materials, blogs, podcasts, and long-form journalism. This appendix includes sources listed in Chapter 3 as well as several more that are not discussed there.

The danger of including such resources in a print publication is that the list will quickly become outdated. This appendix should serve not only as a guide to specific resources, but also as an example for the types of resources that exist for instructors using a case study approach.

Open Access Materials

Barolsky, Daniel and Louis Epstein, general editors. *Open Access Musicology*. https://openaccessmusicology.wordpress.com/. Article-length studies by specialists written for undergraduate students. Peer reviewed by scholars and students.

Fosler-Lussier, Danielle. *Music on the Move*. University of Michigan Press, 2020. www.fulcrum.org/concern/monographs/m613n040s. Textbook. Includes case studies from a global perspective.

Global Jukebox. https://theglobaljukebox.org/#. Wide variety of resources including guided tours though world music styles and geographies.

Morgan-Ellis, Esther M., editor. *Resonances: Engaging Music in Its Cultural Context*. University of North Georgia Press, 2020. https://ung.edu/university-press/books/resonances-engaging-music.php. Textbook. Case studies organized by functions and/or contexts of the music. Includes listening guides and sources for further reading.

Music of Asian America Research Center. College Music Society. http://asianamericanmusic.org/cms/. Currently hosts three sets of resources: (1) Asian America Through 22 Songs, (2) Lesson Plans for

High School Students (in collaboration with Smithsonian Folkways), and (3) Oral Histories. Features Asian American music and musicians from a wide variety of styles and practices.

Nielsen, Kristina, Jessie Vallejo, and Christopher Witulski, general editors. *World Music Textbook.* https://worldmusictextbook.org/. Global case studies written for undergraduate readers. Richly illustrated with embedded audio and video.

Smithsonian Folkways Recordings. https://folkways.si.edu/. Wise variety of articles on musicians and bands with embedded recordings and videos. The "Learn" tab features an interactive map that leads to lesson plans from all over the world. Although the lesson plans are designed for grades K–12, the topics and materials could easily be adapted for case studies.

"WAM! Women and Music." Rutgers Mason Gross School of the Arts. https://wam.rutgers.edu/. Texts and videos on women in classical music. Many videos feature interviews with scholars. Some include sources for further reading.

Blogs

All Music. www.allmusic.com/blog. Features interviews with musicians.

The Avid Listener, https://theavidlistenerblog.com/. Various authors. Hosted by W. W. Norton and designed to supplement *A History of Western Music* and other print textbooks with more diverse materials.

Deceptive Cadence from NPR Classical. www.npr.org/blogs/deceptive cadence/. New music news and reviews as well as long-form obituaries. Audio broadcasts often included. Various authors.

Naxos Musicology International, www.naxosmusicology.com/. Writing from various authors on a wide variety of musical topics. Accessible only with a subscription to Naxos Music Library.

New Music Box, https://newmusicusa.org/newmusicbox/. Online magazine devoted to new music composers, performers, and issues related to the politics of contemporary music.

Ross, Alex. *Alex Ross: The Rest is Noise.* www.therestisnoise.com/. *New Yorker* music critic and author. Includes in-depth discussions as well as reviews of recent concerts, recordings, and books.

Video Resources

Brandon Acker. www.youtube.com/channel/UC-GiI_5U-WkPIKqsq056 wvg. Plucked string discussions, demonstrations, and performances.

Classical Nerd. www.youtube.com/channel/UCPLwlOq7DU_3J60Y
d99jXSA. Entertaining lectures on many canonic classical music
topics, composers, and performers.

Early Music Sources. www.youtube.com/channel/UCJOiqToQ7kia
kqTLE7Hdd5g. Lectures and demonstrations on early music performance problems, compositional issues, composers, and pieces.

Keep it Classical. www.youtube.com/c/KeepitClassical. Lectures on
mostly canonical topics organized by style periods.

Orchestra of the Age of Enlightenment. www.youtube.com/c/Orchestra
oftheAgeofEnlightenment. Performances, introductions to historical
instruments, and lectures on performance issues and practices.

Podcasts

Afropop Worldwide, https://afropop.org/page/podcasts. Discussions of
the music of Africa and the African diaspora.

American Songster, www.wunc.org/podcast/american-songster-radio.
Histories of the stories, songs, and poetry of Black cowboys, hosted
by Dom Flemons.

Aria Code, www.npr.org/podcasts/674248483/aria-code. Discussions of
specific arias with critics, performers, conductors, and musicologists,
hosted by Rhiannon Giddens.

Classically Speaking, www.npr.org/podcasts/659942207/classically-
speaking. Hosted by Colleen Phelps; interviews with composers,
conductors, and performers of classical music in Nashville.

Dissect, https://dissectpodcast.com/. Deep-dive analysis of an album
over the course of a season.

Hearing the Pulitzers, https://hearingthepulitzers.podbean.com/. Year-
by-year discussion of the Pulitzer Prize winning compositions, hosted
by Andrew Granade and David Thurmaier.

Meet the Composer, www.npr.org/podcasts/528124256/meet-the-compo
ser. Each episode is devoted to a composer, work, or musical scene
with extended musical examples in "bonus tracks."

Society for Ethnomusicology's Ethnomusicology Today, www.ethn
omusicology.org/members/group_content_view.asp?group=156
353&id=534562. Discussions with authors of articles published in
Ethnomusicology.

Song Exploder, https://songexploder.net/podcast. Songwriters, produ-
cers, and composers analyze a specific work and describe the creation
process.

Sound Expertise, https://soundexpertise.org/. Interviews with
musicologists about their research on diverse topics.

Appendix 3: Sample Case Study Narrative

The following case study narrative demonstrates how one might adapt a scholarly article as a case study narrative. Javier Marín-López's article "The Musical Inventory of Mexico Cathedral, 1589: A Lost Document Rediscovered" was published in *Early Music* in 2008. In general, I have simplified the language and deleted detail that was not essential to the larger argument. However, in some cases I added information that will help students locate sources discussed in the article. I did not clutter the text with definitions, although there are many terms that undergraduates will likely have to look up. I find it essential to state the author's research question(s) as such in the introduction. Ending the narrative with a question or problem to jump-start the discussion is also a good strategy, although it is not one that I have employed here.

This case study on the 1589 musical inventory of the Mexico Cathedral is adaptable. It could be used with students at a variety of levels and in different types of courses. The music discussed in the narrative is quite sophisticated. On the one hand, it could serve to simply introduce students to important sixteenth-century polyphonic genres and some of the major renaissance composers without requiring a deep study of compositional processes and forms. On the other hand, it could frame a deeper study of the music, especially given the accessibility of many of the editions discussed in the narrative. An added benefit of this case study is that the focus on Spanish repertories in a New Spanish colony adds a global perspective to the traditional study of renaissance polyphony. This case study is also an ideal way to introduce bibliographic tools such as *RISM*.

The Mexico City Cathedral Musical Inventory of 1589

The Fall of Tenochtitlan in 1521 was a decisive event in the Spanish conquest of the Aztec Empire. The Spanish conquistador Hernán

Cortés manipulated local factions and exploited pre-existing political divisions with the help of indigenous allies in order to establish control over what was called "New Spain." Shortly afterward, Cortés made Mexico City the new political, religious, and economic capital of New Spain. The first printing press of the New World was set up there in 1539 and the Royal and Pontifical University was founded in 1553 for the New Spanish intellectual elites. A cathedral was built on the site of the legendary Aztec temple and was made an archdiocese in 1546.

Historians—especially Mexican musicologists—have documented the exceptionally vibrant musical life of Mexico City during this early colonial period.[1] In the 1940s, the American musicologist Robert Stevenson found centuries-old books of polyphonic music in the Mexico City Cathedral and has written several studies on the significance of the Mexico Cathedral in the musical life of the city.[2] An important source of study for future scholarship is an inventory of the cathedral's musical treasures written in 1589, which includes descriptions of the two cathedral organs and a detailed list of books of polyphonic music. This inventory was misplaced in the 1940s but was rediscovered by musicologist Javier Marín-López in the early 2000s.[3]

What might we learn about the musical life in a colonial cathedral in the sixteenth century from such an inventory? How might the cathedral have come to own such expensive books of music? What might the collection tell us about the colonialists' continued ties to Europe? And what might the inventory tell us about relationships between the New Spanish colonialists and indigenous Mexicans?

The Repertoire of the Inventory

It's not clear who made the inventory. Marín-López guesses that the singer and chapelmaster Juan Hernández might have written it as he was responsible for the music books at the time it was created. Hernández also collected and copied music and even composed himself, although none of the works in the inventory are attributed to him.

The inventory of books of polyphony includes 208 entries by 11 composers in a wide range of musical genres. According to the inventory, the cathedral's collection included large choirbooks, smaller partbooks—both printed and in manuscript—and works copied out on loose sheets of paper. The works in this collection are both sacred works in Latin and vernacular music in the colonial Spanish dialect, Castilian.

Printed Collections of Polyphony

Some entries in the inventory provide not only the composer's name and the musical genre (e.g., Mass, motet, etc.), but also provide the publishing details (the city, publisher, and date). Given this information, it's possible to get a relatively clear picture of the polyphonic music library in the Mexico Cathedral (see Table A.3.1).

For scholars of renaissance polyphony, it is likely not surprising to see music by Tomás Luis de Victoria and Cristóbal de Morales included in the inventory. Both composers are among the most well-known and widely published Spanish composers of their day. The four volumes by Victoria listed in the inventory contain Masses, Magnificats, antiphons, hymns, psalms, and motets—the main genres of Latin, sacred polyphony. These volumes came to Mexico City shortly after their publication and, when compared to the holdings of other cathedrals at the time, the Mexico Cathedral in 1589 held one of the largest collections of Victoria's music in the world. The two books of masses by Morales were widely disseminated in Spain and its colonies and are included in the inventories of public and private libraries throughout South America.

Pedro and Francisco Guerrero are also Spanish composers, and although they are not as well-known today, their music (especially Francisco's) was used in liturgical settings in Mexico until the eighteenth century.

The "foreign" composers included in the inventory include the Franco-Flemish composers Pierre Colin, whose music is rarely found in sixteenth-century Spanish inventories, and Josquin, who is perhaps the most well-known renaissance composer, and whose music appears most frequently in Spanish inventories.

Some of the entries in the inventory are more difficult to identify, such as four partbooks of motets described as "de la flor" ("of the flower," or *Motteti del fiore*). Several such volumes were published by Jacques Moderne in Lyon between 1532 and 1542 and by Antonio Gardano in Venice in 1545. Even though we cannot confidently say which of these editions was in the Mexico Cathedral library, all of them had similar contents, containing motets by Franco-Flemish composers such as Arcadelt, Cortois, Gombert, Lassus, and Willaert. The ten partbooks are equally a mystery. The inventory simply says that the items were partbooks ("pequeños"), that they were printed ("de molde"), that they contained motets by a variety of authors ("de diversos autores"), and that they had lettering in gilt. Many such editions from Italy or France existed.

Table A.3.1 Printed books of polyphony in the Mexico Cathedral inventory

Date	Composer	Title	City	Publisher	RISM A1 or B1#
unknown	not specified	4 partbooks of motets	unknown	unknown	unknown
unknown	not specified	5 partbooks of masses and motets	unknown	unknown	unknown
unknown	not specified	10 partbooks of motets (probably two collections)	unknown	unknown	unknown
1532	not specified[a]	Liber Viginti Missarum	Paris	Pierre Attaingnant	1532|1–7
?1532	not specified	Motteti del fiore	?Lyon	?Jacques Moderne	?1532|9
1541	Pierre Colin	Liber Octo Missarum	Lyon	Jacques Moderne	C 3307
1544	Cristóbal de Morales	Missarum Liber Primus	Rome	Valerio Dorico & Lodovico fratres	M 3580
1544	Cristóbal de Morales	Missarum Liber Secundus	Rome	Valerio Dorico & Lodovico fratres	M 3582
?1551–5	Pedro Guerrero	Liber Primus Epigramatum	?Seville	?Martín de Montesdoca	not listed in RISM
1555	Francisco Guerrero	Sacrae cantiones	Seville	Martín de Montesdoca	G 4867
1566	Francisco Guerrero	Liber Primus Missarum	Paris	Nicolas Du Chemin	G 4870
1570	Francisco Guerrero	Motteta	Venice	Antonio Gardano, figliuoli	G 4871
1581	Tomás Luis de Victoria	Hymni totius anni ... cum quattuor psalmis	Rome	Francesco Zannetti	V 1428
1581	Tomás Luis de Victoria	Cantica B. Virginis vulgo magnificat ... cum quatuor antiphonis	Rome	Francesco Zannetti	V 1430
1583	Tomás Luis de Victoria	Missarum libri duo	Rome	Alessandro Gardano	V 1431
1585	Tomás Luis de Victoria	Motecta festorum totius anni	Rome	Alessandro Gardano	V 1433 / 1585|6

a Although the inventory does not include the names of the composers in this collection, we can identify its contents from surviving prints. This collection includes works by Josquin, Sermisy, Gascogne, Manchicourt, Mouton, Richafort, Divitis, Prioris, Gombert, and others.

What we find in the inventory is that the cathedral had an extensive, varied, and international repertory that must have been acquired through different channels. We have evidence that Morales and Victoria sent their music to cathedrals in the New World themselves, and this may have been the case with the Mexico Cathedral. The French and Italian polyphonic books may have been given as gifts to the cathedral from high-ranking clergymen. Such gifts were given as tokens of gratitude or as a means to win favor with the high-ranking archbishop.

The unidentified ten partbooks are a good example of such a gift. The inventory tells us that they were "presented by his worship" ("que regaló su señoría"). The gift was most likely made by the archbishop Pedro de Moya Contreras (d. 1591), a major musical patron who was also the Viceroy and General Inquisitor of New Spain. There is no evidence that Moya Contreras traveled to Italy, but he was in constant contact by correspondence with the Holy See through Francisco Beteta, canon of Puebla Cathedral, who represented the Mexican hierarchy in Rome. Beteta was also apparently a bookseller and publisher. It is wholly possible, following well-established practice, that Beteta might have returned to Mexico with printed music books and presented them to Moya Contreras as a gift of gratitude.

Manuscript Collections of Latin Polyphony

In addition to the printed books of polyphony, the inventory lists 21 manuscript collections (10 in choirbook format, 11 in partbooks). The inventory does not list the specific contents of each collection in detail, nor does it typically include the composer's name; rather, the inventory lists the repertory included in each: motets; Masses; music for Holy Week (with psalms, Passions and Lamentations); music for the Mass and Office of the Dead; music for Vespers including psalms; Magnificats; hymns; and others. Despite the fact that few composers are mentioned in the inventory, we do get a vivid picture of the variety of music that was required for worship services in the cathedral and the types of polyphony that were regularly performed there. We also can see from the inventory a close relationship between print and manuscript sources, as people copied by hand from print sources music that was needed for the worship service.

Devotional Music

In addition to a large number of Latin-texted works, the inventory includes a large repertory of pieces with Castilian texts, including 39 collections in bound notebooks and 109 pieces copied in parts or on separate sheets. Much of this music was paraliturgical; that is, it was performed as a supplement to the Mass—both inside and outside of the cathedral—and for special feast days. Given the ephemeral nature of this repertoire, it is unusual that it was catalogued at all. Unfortunately, the names of the composers are not included in the inventory; we do have, however, the first words of the text, the number of voices, the genre, and the name of the feast day for which it was written.

Although none of this music has survived, the inventory helps illuminate an otherwise obscure aspect of music making in the New Spanish colonies in the sixteenth century. Much of this music was used in public theatrical productions organized by churches, towns, and religious orders (especially the Jesuits). These performances were meant to teach people about Christianity, but were also used as political propaganda. They were often simply part of civic celebrations.

We have evidence that Lázaro del Álamo, the chapelmaster of the Mexico Cathedral between 1556 and 1570, wrote motets, villancicos, and "chanzonetas" for theatrical events to celebrate the Feast of Corpus Cristi and Christmas. The following chapelmaster, Juan de Vitoria (1570–1574), directed and probably composed incidental music for two theatrical works created to celebrate the appointment of the new archbishop in 1574. The chapelmaster following Vitoria wrote several pieces for festivities to celebrate the gift of some relics presented to the local Jesuits from the pope in 1578. This archival evidence makes it clear that the local chapelmasters were expected to compose new music for such public theatrical celebrations.

In addition to these extraordinarily special occasions, vernacular genres, especially villancicos and chanzonetas, were a normal part of the liturgical year. Both genres were especially popular, accounting for 90 percent of the vernacular pieces in the inventory, and despite the fact that no composers are named in the inventory we can assume that much of the music was composed "in house." The statutes of Mexico Cathedral (1585) indicate that the chapelmaster was expected to compose "devout and honest songs" ("canciones devotas y honestas") for Christmas, Epiphany, Corpus Christi, Assumption, and several saints' days, including the feast days of the local patron saints of Mexico City. Indeed, the cathedral even granted the chapelmaster time off from regular duties in order to seek out texts and set them to music, and the amount of leave granted corresponded to the importance of the feast day. Popular characters appear in these texts with names such as Gil, Juana, Carrillo, Manuel, and Mexía.

The *coloquio* was another popular vernacular genre. It was a religious drama in the form of a dialogue designed for instruction. The typical coloquio was a series of questions and answers, and composers usually used double choirs for the dialogue effect.

Based on the inventory, the opening lines of a sample coloquio begins with the text "Muerte, ¿de quién huides, di?" ("Death, say, from whom are you fleeing?") "De la vida que hoy es nascida" ("From the life that is born today.") Although none of this music still exists, Marín-Lopéz concludes that it must have been similar to Gaspar Fernandes's *Cancionero* musical, which includes largely homorhythmic textures and antiphonal settings of two choirs, with the play between question and answer having an almost theatrical effect. The polychoral coloquio demonstrates how polychoral settings, which developed at the end of the sixteenth century and were typically associated with the city of Venice, were neither reserved for Latin settings nor confined to Europe.

Conclusion

Despite the inevitable limitations of an analysis based on an inventory from the archives of a single cathedral, it is possible to get a glimpse of the polyphonic repertory performed in a New World cathedral in the sixteenth century. We see a juxtaposition of works by Iberian composers, such as Victoria and Morales, with works by "foreign" composers, especially Franco-Flemish ones, such as Josquin. We also find a very lively and productive home-grown practice of composition for special events inside and outside of the cathedral. And when compared to other cathedral collections, we learn that the Mexico Cathedral's music library was one of the richest in America, a clear reflection of the city's position as a cosmopolitan center and a meeting-point for the music that circulated in every region of the Spanish empire.

This case study is based on Javier Marín-López, "The Musical Inventory of Mexico Cathedral, 1589: A Lost Document Rediscovered," *Early Music* 36, no. 4 (November 2008): 575–596.

Sample Questions for Discussion

1   The narrative compares the holdings of the Mexico Cathedral music library to those of other cathedrals or other private collections from the same time period. How can we learn about the holdings of sixteenth-century collections in the Americas such as the one in the narrative? How is it possible to compare the holdings of one library to another?

2   Can you find facsimiles of some of the printed collections listed in the table? What do you notice about how they are printed? What about how they are notated? Is it possible to sing some of this polyphony from this printed edition?

3   How does a print publication, such as the ones listed in the table, influence how we value a composer? Or how does it shape what we know about the composer? Compare what we know about the composers in the table to what we know about the ones that we suspect are included in the manuscript collections or in the collections of devotional music.

4   The opening paragraph radically understates the consequences of the Spanish conquest for the Aztecs. Could it be that the music listed in the inventory participates in the power structures that perpetrated what amounted to Aztec cultural genocide? Why or why not? If so, how?

Notes

1   See Gabriel Saldívar, *Historia de la música en México épocas precortesiana y colonial* (Mexico City: Secretaría de Educación Pública, Departamento de Bellas Artes, 1934); Jesús Estrada, *Música y músicos de la época virreinal* (Mexico City: Secretaría de Educación Pública, 1973); and Jaime González-Quinoñes, *Villancicos y cantatas mexicanos del siglo XVIII* (Mexico City: UNAM, Escuela Nacional de Música, 1990).

2   See Robert Stevenson, *Music in Mexico. A Historical Survey* (New York: Thomas Y. Crowell Company, 1952), 100–122 and 138–158; *Music in Aztec and Inca Territory* (Berkeley: University of California Press, 1968), 154–240; "Mexico City Cathedral: The Founding Century," *Inter-American Music Review* (1979): 131–179.

3   Javier Marín-López, "The Musical Inventory of Mexico Cathedral, 1589: A Lost Document Rediscovered," *Early Music* 36, no. 4 (November 2008): 575–596.

Appendix 4: Research Questions in Published Scholarship

The excerpts below are taken from the opening paragraph(s) of a scholarly article or book. Each contains the research question stated as such. Each example demonstrates scholarly inquiry at a very high level, yet each is motivated by a sense of curiosity and/or a keen awareness of a musicological problem.

Bonta, Stephen. "The Uses of the Sonata da Chiesa." *Journal of the American Musicological Society* 22, no. 1 (Spring, 1969): 54–84.

In spite of the popularity of the *sonata da chiesa*, evident in the innumerable collections published in Italy from its first appearance around 1650 up through 1700, information is all but non-existent on its specific employment in the Roman Rite during this period. Attempts to supply answers on its use have been hampered thus far by inadequate consideration of the larger question of the role of non-liturgical pieces—both vocal and instrumental—in the Divine Offices in the seventeenth century. Those writers suggesting answers have been unable to explain adequately just how such non-liturgical pieces fitted into the service. Were instrumental pieces used as preludes or postludes to liturgical chants? Were instrumental or vocal pieces used as substitutes for these chants? And, if so, what happened to the liturgical texts of these chants?

Green, Emily H. "How to Read a Rondeau: On Pleasure, Analysis, and the Desultory in Amateur Performance Practice of the Eighteenth Century." *Journal of the American Musicological Society* 73, no. 2 (Summer 2020): 267–325.

Consider … a reading of eighteenth-century music that would suit a [casual, quotidian] context. Surely no one would attempt to play music while enduring the prodding of a friseur, but without doubt, gentle people do use music to pass the time, particularly at home in the waning light of the day, particularly after the arrival of guests, and, to be perfectly candid, particularly when such guests display poor verbal comportment. Could *those* irksome hours be made pleasurable with an equally casual reading of music? And if so, what sort of reading would it be?

Hisama, Ellie. "John Zorn and the Postmodern Condition." In *Locating East Asia in Western Art Music.* Edited by Yayoi Uno Everett and Frederick Lau, 72–84. Middletown, CT: Wesleyan University Press, 2004.

To study music for which we have great affection is how we music theorists tend to occupy our professional lives, spending months or years with a body of musical works or with a single piece of music in order to describe its properties and to ponder why it has the power to move us. But what of music that we don't care for, what of music that we find dull, inept, or downright repulsive? What of music that we understand to negate, devalue, and disrespect who we are?

To address these questions, I shall explore the music of the saxophonist and composer John Zorn as it engages me in three overlapping ways—as a woman, as an Asian-American (specifically as a North American of Japanese descent), and as a theorist.

Robin, William. "Balance Problems: Music in the American University and Ensemble." *Journal of the American Musicological Society* 71, no. 3 (Fall 2018): 749–793.

[Robin's article opens with an anecdote about a collaboration between the singer-songwriter Ben Folds and the sextet chamber ensemble yMusic at Duke University.]

In his 1958 polemic "Who Cares If You Listen?" Milton Babbitt imagines the American academy as "a home for the 'complex,' 'difficult,' and 'problematical' in music." What has changed since Babbitt's infamous essay, such that a collaboration between doctoral composition students and a rock musician was regarded as neither outré nor extracurricular, but was instead officially sponsored by the music department of an elite university?

Robinson, Dylan. *Hungry Listening: Resonant Theory for Indigenous Sound Studies.* Minneapolis: University of Minnesota Press, 2020.

The Eskimos are such an astonishingly unmusical race that the composer really has to wring his material to make it musically presentable. There is a marked similarity between an Eskimo singing and Sir Winston Churchill clearing his throat.

—R. Murray Schafer, "On the Limits of
Nationalism in Canadian Music" (1961)

What can we hear through Schafer's description of Inuit throat singing? Does your aural imagination (or audiation) hear such astonishingly unmusical voices, a requiem for Winston Churchill clearing his throat? Do Schafer's words sonify compositional violence—the "wringing" of Inuit voices? Can you hear settler desire for Indigenous "present-ability" or "civility" as Indigenous throat songs (games) are processed through settler colonial musical logic? Or perhaps is it impossible to hear anything beyond Schafer's own voice, with its opinionated rhythm, its racist timbre. *Hungry Listening* focuses on a range of encounters between Indigenous song and Western art music (also called classical music or concert music) such as the one described in Schafer's writing. It examines how we listen to such encounters in the moment of their sounding, and how writing allows certain moments of sonic experience to be heard while foreclosing upon others. Additionally, at various points through this book I ask you to consider the relationships you have with particular voices—how your positionality guides the way you listen to musical subjectivity.

Index